internet cool guide™

CONTENTS

RATINGS

c content

d design

s customer service

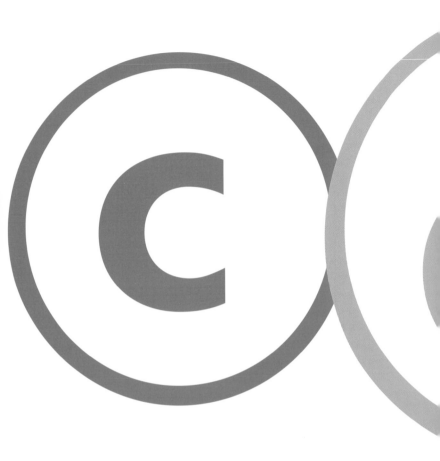

INTRODUCTION

Ah, the luxuries of shopping online: no irritating salespeople, no lines, no driving. Is it just us, or do the malls feel a little emptier these days? With over 40,000 online stores (and counting), it's difficult to think of a product you *can't* buy directly from your desktop—and we're talking everything from flowers to ice cream to luxury autos.

In the following pages, we've selected 600 of the coolest shopping sites on the Web—hand-picked for security, superior customer service, and compelling content. You'll also find information on a few of the best innovations in online shopping—everything from auctions to shopping bots—along with all the need-to-know information on how to shop safely.

How the Sites are Chosen

Internet Cool Guide editors are constantly scouring the Web to find the hottest sites and services around, researching thousands of e-commerce sites to bring you the small collection here. What do we look for in a Web site? For starters, every site in the book offers secure online ordering. We also check for stellar customer service, search capabilities, extensive and easy-to-read help pages, a privacy policy, a toll-free customer service phone number, detailed product descriptions, a sophisticated and user-friendly design—and of course, a ton of great products for sale.

How the Ratings Are Assigned

Rating symbols are assigned to sites that are particularly outstanding in any of three areas: content, design, or customer service.

The content rating indicates that the site offers information such as side-by-side product comparisons, feature articles, or other interactive tools (like wish lists and customizable pages).

The design rating is awarded to sites that combine cutting-edge graphics with a user-friendly, well-organized layout. These sites also provide large, zoomable pictures of their products and take you through the checkout process in just a few clicks.

Sites that receive the customer service symbol excel at making the shopping experience smooth and hassle-free. They have detailed help pages and generous return policies, are super-responsive to phone calls and questions, and offer a toll-free phone number, a privacy policy, order confirmations, and in some cases, free shipping.

TOP TIPS FOR SAFE E-SHOPPING

We all know that online shopping is easier than schlepping to the local mall. But with the added convenience have come new problems: late deliveries, clothes that don't fit properly, and worries about credit card security, personal privacy, and scams. The following guidelines can help you determine whether an e-commerce site is worth your time (and money).

Do business with companies you know and trust.

It always feels safer to do business with a company you've heard of, like Williams-Sonoma or The Gap, so these are the places to start if you're wary or inexperienced with online shopping. Shopping with a brick-and-mortar company may have added advantages—most of them will allow you to return products you've purchased online to a local store. Of course, that's not to say you shouldn't patronize new or small e-commerce sites (they're everywhere!)—just be sure to check them out thoroughly before you buy.

Check for a seal of approval from a consumer group like the Better Business Bureau.

If a site has been awarded the BBB's Reliability Seal, they have a proven record of providing merchandise in good quality and in a reasonable time period. Many other reliability seals have proliferated on the Web, including the TRUSTe seal (which rates a site's privacy policy, not service or security), the BizRate seal (an unbiased and reliable measure of e-commerce worthiness), and the Certified Safe Shopping seal. Most of these will allow you to click through to a report on the company.

Be sure the site offers secure ordering.

Any information you submit to a Web site—your credit card number, name, address, and phone number—should be sent through a secure server. That way, sensitive information will be encrypted (or scrambled), making it nearly impossible to steal. There are two ways to check if you are on a secure page. The first is to look for a small padlock icon at the bottom of your browser window—if it's locked, the page uses Secure Socket Layer (SSL) encryption, and you can proceed safely. Also check the address bar for the page's URL—it should begin with https://, rather than http://. That little "s" makes a big difference!

Be sure that the company's phone number and physical address are listed on the site.

This is crucial in case something goes wrong down the line: you want to be sure that if there are problems with your order—or it never arrives—you can get a human being on the phone. Most sites will provide an e-mail address for you to submit questions or concerns; sometimes, though, that impersonal e-mail form just isn't enough. If a company doesn't provide contact information on its site (shame, shame), look it up at www.dotcomdirectory.com.

Read the site's privacy policy.

Seems you can't buy anything online these days without filling out a form full of unnecessary personal information, including your name, address, phone number, e-mail address, and personal preferences (for starters). On the one hand, this information can help companies serve you better, allowing them to tailor the content and advertising on a site to your specific tastes. But this information can easily get into the wrong hands—some companies may sell your stats to third-parties. What does this mean for you? Well, it could mean a flood of junk mail or e-mail, or even worse, someone else knowing exactly how you're spending your money.

Before submitting any information to a site, read the privacy statement carefully. The best vendors will indicate that they won't sell, rent, or share information about you, no matter what. Other companies won't sell your personal data, but might share aggregate data— so while they won't tell anyone that you bought 18 pounds of head cheese from www.freakymeats.com last month, they might say that three various people bought 250 pounds of head cheese total. You may also run into a privacy policy full of incomprehensible legalese, or something like Amazon.com's policy, which states that Amazon.com may resell customer data to "trustworthy third parties." (We're still not sure who those "trustworthy" parties are.) If you find (or fear) that your name has been rented or sold to other companies, contact a non-profit group such as the Coalition Against Unsolicited Commercial Email (www.cauce.org) or the Mail Abuse Prevention System (www.mail-abuse.org) for further advice.

Always pay with plastic.

If a site doesn't take credit cards, you may want to take your money elsewhere. In the rare case that something goes wrong with your order, your credit card company probably offers insurance against fraudulent charges. If you fear having your credit card numbers lost in the ether, keep in mind two simple guidelines: first, always enter your credit card number on a secure page (see above). Second, never send your credit card number to anyone in an e-mail message.

Keep a watchful eye on the mini-shoppers.

Unfortunately—or fortunately if you're an Internet savvy kid—anyone can ring up a bill online if they have the necessary ingredients: card number, expiration date, and billing address. You may want to set ground rules for your kids to be sure they're spending wisely online (if at all)—unless you don't mind the unexpected bill for 100 new CDs and an e-pizza. A slew of new sites, such as www.icanbuy.com, let parents set up online allowances for their children. Parents provide their credit card numbers and indicate the monthly amount; then kids get to spend the money at sites like dELiAs.cOm and CDNOW. Some of these sites (like www.doughnet.com) will also help teens set up online bank accounts and provide real-life financial advice on topics like saving and giving to charity.

In case something goes wrong . . .

Say you find a lovely, green cashmere sweater online at www.themostbeautifulsweaterintheworld.com. You've checked for security, given your credit card number and shipping address, and been told by an automated message that your order was accepted. When your sweater arrives, chances are it's exactly what you ordered. Maybe the color looks a little bolder in the harsh light of day than it did on your computer screen, but basically you've gotten what you paid for. Great. This is what you can expect most of the time you shop online.

But what about the rest of the time? You open the box and the sweater is nylon, fraying at the seams, and way too long. Or, even worse, you wait as two weeks become four and the sweater never arrives. What can you do?

- Keep a record of all your communication with an e-commerce company, including your credit card statement and a printout of the window showing the finalized sale.

- If anything goes wrong, contact the company directly. Most times, misunderstandings can be worked out with a simple phone call. If calling doesn't work, send a letter indicating that you are serious about resolving the matter, and include a copy of your order verification.

- If you suspect delinquency or out-and-out fraud, contact the Better Business Bureau Online (www.bbbonline.org), which can provide mediation, informal dispute settlement, or even legal help. They can also help you file and track a complaint against the company. The National Fraud Information Center/Internet Fraud Watch (www.fraud.org) helps consumers distinguish between legitimate and fraudulent Internet offers, tracks and files complaints against companies, and reports suspected fraud to appropriate law enforcement agencies. Call their toll-free number (1-800-876-7060) for help if you feel you've been swindled.

- If you've had a negative experience with an online store, you may want to post your experience at a consumer information site like BizRate.com. That way, you help other online shoppers steer clear of bad service or scams, and keep stores accountable for their service.

Hot Bots!

Toss out the coupon circulars—with price comparison engines (also called "shopping bots") cropping up like bunnies, it's a whole lot easier to find bargains on the Web. How does it work? And which bots are best at finding deals?

Let's start with the basics. A shopping bot is basically an electronic gopher–type in the item you're searching for, and it runs from e-store to e-store checking which ones have it and how much it costs at each site. In one quick search you'll be able to see how much the latest Harry Potter adventure costs at a bevy of online bookstores. Sort by price, and you'll see clearly which one offers the best deal. Click on the product link, and you go straight to the checkout page at the site you've chosen. Easy, right?

Well, sort of. Keep in mind that bot technology is still in its infancy; it doesn't yet offer the kind of pricing intelligence that would take into account whether a merchant charges restocking fees on returns (thereby undoing your deal). Some bots don't even provide information on shipping charges, which can make a big difference on a small purchase like a book or CD.

Also keep in mind that comparison bots are only as good as the extent of their search engines. So if a bot only searches a limited list of merchants, the prices may not be the lowest available. Some sites offer merchants a prominent place on their lists in exchange for a fee–or only search merchants that pay to be listed. In the case of Amazon.com's price comparison feature, All Products Search, you'll find that you can only compare prices on items that Amazon doesn't carry. So for books, music, and other Amazon.com mainstays, you can't compare prices at Barnes & Noble or CDNOW.

Reservations aside, shopping bots are amazing little money- and time-saving tools, and are getting more sophisticated by the minute. Some (like DealTime.com) can notify you by cell phone or e-mail when they find the price you want on a particular product. Others (like DealPilot Express) shop the Web along with you, comparing prices in a window adjacent to your browser. EBoodle, which bills itself as a "personal shopping assistant," compares prices in a companion window and can even fill out forms automatically at the checkout page.

The better shopping bots also offer consumer information and buying guides, so you can figure out which fax machine or cordless phone is right for you before committing to a model with features that you don't want or need.

A Quick Guide to Online Price Comparisons

Use an independent bot.

Sites like mySimon and PriceScan are independent bots, meaning that they aren't sponsored by a particular company or brand, and don't accept money from vendors to be listed. You're usually better off going to sites like these to comparison shop—but be aware that even independent sites may charge companies to be listed at the top of the search results. Be sure to scroll through all the listings or re-sort them by price or brand.

Make your search as specific as possible.

A general search for a VCR or a camera may turn up a jumble of different models and brands, all of varying quality. So before you choose the lowest price, figure out which particular camera best suits your needs and perform a search for that specific model. The best bots should offer product reviews and side-by-side comparisons of different products. For clothing, try specifying brands (e.g. "DKNY black dress") rather than general product categories (e.g. "dress").

Format your search correctly.

Just like the search engines, each price comparison site has its own protocol for searches. Some (bottomdollar.com, for example) suggest putting phrase names like "Red Hot Chili Peppers" in quotes. Others match all the keywords in your search regardless of quotes. It's worth it to spend a few minutes learning the lingo when using a site for the first time.

Try your search on a few different bots.

As with all online bargain hunting, the more you search, the better deals you will find. You may want to start out searching a general bot like Jango, then move to a more specialized engine like GEMM (for music and videos), or CNET's Shopper.com (for computer products).

You'll also notice that most bots require you to click on a general product category before you type in your search terms. Sometimes it's difficult to determine which category your product fits into—for example, digital movie cameras might fall under "electronics" or "computers." If you're having trouble figuring it out, just move on to another site—it may be better organized.

Compare shipping prices and return policies before you buy.

Aside from price, there are plenty of factors that can influence your buying decision. You may decide to pay a higher price for a brand you trust, or for a store that offers free shipping and free returns.

Going Once ... Going Twice ...

Haven't gotten in on the online auctions yet? What are you waiting for? Between giants like eBay and hundreds of small collector's auctions, you can name your price for just about anything you never knew you wanted.

That's right. Online auction fever is hotter than ever, and new and ever more specialized auction sites are setting up shop all the time. The upside? You'll find oodles of cool stuff for sale: score a Renoir print, a new camera, or that *Star Wars* lunchbox you've always wanted. The downside? You may end up paying twice the actual value for a beat-up lunchbox that's so chipped you can't even see Luke's feathered hair. No worries—with a little auction know-how, you'll soon be bidding with the best of them.

The Golden Rule

Know what you want to spend. It's easy to get caught up in the competitive frenzy of the auctions (especially if you're a first-timer), but much more difficult to part with your hard-earned dollars once you've laid down last week's paycheck for a lock of Loni Anderson's hair. Remember: this isn't a game.

Learning the Territory

There are two basic types of auctions: person-to-person and store-to-person. The most well-known auctions, like eBay and Yahoo! Auctions, fall into the first category. Here, the auction site acts as a host for individuals to buy and sell to each other. Individual sellers choose the auction format they'd like to use (Reserve Price, Private, Dutch, or Restricted-Access—see our auction glossary for further details on each type) and are responsible for sending the merchandise to the highest bidder. If a seller fails to deliver the merchandise, buyers can take action against the individual seller but not against the auction site itself. In store-to-person auctions, a company puts items up for sale in an auction forum. Store-to-person auctions can mean big discounts, but beware: sometimes stores will put an item up for auction at a starting bid that is the same as, or just slightly lower than, its usual price. You could actually end up paying more than if you had bought the item at retail!

Choices, Choices

Which auction site should you use? It depends on who you are and what you're looking for. First-timers who want to get their feet wet should start with eBay or Yahoo! Auctions—sites that have clear, easy-to-read instructions and tons of categories to browse.

If you're searching for a particular type of merchandise (like jewelry, antiques, or art), you may want to try a specialty auction site. (Locate one at www.auctionrover.com.) These sites will have a finely tuned selection of items rather than just one or two random choices. You'll also find that the action is quieter at these sites than on the big names—great if you're inclined to mull over a bid before you lay it down. Also check out auction search engines such as Bidder's Edge (www.biddersedge.com). Here, you enter the item you're looking for and the site searches for it across a number of different auction sites. This is especially helpful if you know exactly what you want and don't have all day to search each individual auction site.

Know Who You're Dealing With

No matter what auction site you choose, take steps to ensure that the person (or company) you're doing business with is ethical, and that you have some recourse if things don't go as planned.

· **Use a reputable auction site.** How to tell: is the site a member of the Better Business Bureau or a similar online reliability program? (Find out at www.bbbonline.com.) Are they profiled on BizRate.com? Is there a business address and phone number listed on the site?

· **Read the fine print.** The fine print holds info you'll want to know in case something goes wrong. Some sites (eBay for example) will reimburse you up to $200 if the item you bought never shows up or is not in the condition advertised by the seller. Other sites state that they're only a venue for trading and won't take responsibility for scams.

· **Peruse the feedback.** Most auction sites provide a rating system to let potential buyers know about a seller's track record. So, once you've located those fabulous golf-patterned suspenders for Dad, take a look at what others have to say about the guy who's selling them. If he's got a high feedback rating, chances are you can proceed with confidence.

· For your protection, don't do business with sellers who won't provide their name, street address, and phone number. When purchasing collectibles or any item where the origin of the item may be in doubt (e.g. Princess Diana's bedroom set), you're better off dealing with a reputable merchant who can prove that the merchandise is authentic.

Research, Research, Research

After you've found an item that interests you, and *before* you bid, it's worth doing a little research to be sure you're getting a good deal. When bidding on electronics, clothing, travel gear, or anything that can be bought in a store, switch over to a price comparison site (try www.mysimon.com) or an online consumer guide (such as www.productopia.com) to see what the item sells for elsewhere. To price collectibles and other unusual items, go to a specialty site or discuss the item and price with a more knowledgeable collector.

If you have a question about the condition of the item you're bidding on, don't hesitate to contact the seller directly by e-mail. He or she should respond within a couple of hours. Be especially vigilant when purchasing collectibles—ask for a written statement describing the item and its value.

Setting Your Maximum Bid

Once you've done a bit of research, decide how much you're willing to spend for your item and set your maximum bid. To save you the hassle of bidding manually, the best auctions will proxy bid for you, automatically raising your bid in small increments until your maximum is reached. You can go on about your day—and even turn off the computer—while your bidding continues electronically. If you win when the auction closes, great. If not, you usually get a chance to increase your offer and continue the bidding. This way, you're still in the running if you simply must have that lunchbox, whatever the cost.

Once You Win

If you're the highest bidder when the auction closes, it's your responsibility to contact the seller (he or she should contact you as well) to close the deal. Arrange a firm delivery time and insist that the shipment is insured. Ask about the return policy, too—will the seller refund your money if the item isn't of the quality you expected? Other tips:

- **Pay by credit card whenever possible.** Your credit card company may be able to assist if the sale turns out to be a scam.

- **Use an escrow service.** If you are bidding for items over $200, consider using a service such as iEscrow (www.iescrow.com). Instead of sending your money directly to the seller, you send it to the escrow service, which will hold your money until you have received the item in good condition. Most escrow companies charge a small fee, dependent on the amount of purchase, but it's a smart way to go if you're laying down a large chunk of change.

What To Do if Things Go Wrong

If you're stiffed by a vendor and can't work it out with them directly (always the best option) the quickest and most effective revenge is to give the dealer a negative rating online. Since auction sellers get most of their sales based on the trust and goodwill of the online community, a negative rating, especially if it is corroborated by others, usually spells chapter 11. If you suspect a deliberate misrepresentation or scam, contact the National Fraud Information Center (www.fraud.org), which tracks complaints and can help mediate a dispute.

Glossary of Auction Jargon

bid increment
The amount by which bids are raised each time. This amount is set by the site, which will usually provide a table that explains how the bid increment is determined.

bid retraction
The quickest way to turn nice beanie-selling grandmas into baseball bat-wielding goons. This is when a bidder cancels a bid after it's been placed.

Dutch auction
A tricky auction to master, but an easy way to save money. In Dutch auctions, sellers with many identical items list the number of items they have and the minimum price they'll accept for them. Then bidders specify both a bid price and the quantity they want to buy. When the auction ends, the winners pay the lowest successful bid price for whatever quantity they bid on, even if it's less than what they themselves offered.

final value fee
A.k.a. the auction site's slice of the pie. This is the fee paid by the seller to the site for the completion of the auction. The fee is calculated as a percentage of the final selling price.

private auction
A type of auction that keeps bidders' identities hush-hush by not displaying their e-mail addresses on an item's bidding history. At the end of the auction, only the seller knows who actually bought the item.

proxy bidding
Placing a confidential maximum bid that the automatic bidding server will inch toward but not exceed to keep a bidder in the winning spot. The higher the maximum bid you enter, the better the chance you'll win.

reserve price auction
A type of auction in which a seller registers but doesn't reveal the lowest price he or she is willing to take for an item (generally higher than the minimum bid). To win, a bidder must meet or exceed the reserve price *and* post the highest bid. If no bidders meet the reserve price, neither the seller nor the high bidder have any obligation to complete the transaction.

restricted-access auctions
Restricted-access auctions make it easy to avoid (or find) adult-only items. To access them, you're usually required to register a credit card number.

shilling
Caveat emptor: this is when a seller bids up his or her own item. Shilling is strictly prohibited but sometimes tough to detect.

sniping
Placing a bid seconds before an auction closes. Although sniping is technically legal, it's considered bad auction netiquette. Proxy bidding helps protect against snipers, because the server will automatically enter any higher bids right after a sniper's bid, ensuring a win.

Art & Collectibles

Collectors Universe www.collectors.com
If half a dozen news stories about Beanie Babies (or stamps, or rare cigars, or baseball cards) sounds like a good time, Collectors Universe is for you. A specialized site for collectors of all kinds, it provides auctions, grading and authentication services, and news stories, all categorized by collectible. Don't miss the auction section, where you can bid on goodies like the last seat on the first commercial space flight ($10,000).

Collect.com www.collect.com
Are you the type of collector who'd walk over ground glass to own a Hardy Boys lunch box? Or maybe a rare trading card? Collect.com is an online community with all kinds of information on anything and everything worth hoarding. You can access price guides, find links to dozens of vendors, or even start your own interactive site. Join a discussion forum to ask a pro how much your valuables are really worth.

icollector www.icollector.com ⓒ ⓢ
This impressive site lets you bid for art, antiques, and collectibles at over 200 auction houses from around the world. This is the place to splurge on a vintage Fender guitar or a 19th century Chinese vase (if you can afford to). Icollector is not a person-to-person auction, so you don't have to worry about whether you can trust an unknown seller; in fact, icollector guarantees purchases for up to $50,000 within seven days of receipt. All this, plus resources like the art price guide, put icollector in a league of its own.

TIAS.com Antiques and Collectibles

TIAS.com www.tias.com ⓒ
TIAS.com (aka The Internet Antique Shop) is something like an Internet antiques mall. Click on a category, and TIAS.com recommends online antique dealers that carry the merchandise you seek, be it art deco lighting, stamps, or Disneyana. If you know what you want, TIAS.com's search feature lets you search the collections of over 235 dealers for that distinctive Victorian ring or antique motorcycle.

The Serious Collector www.seriouscollector.com

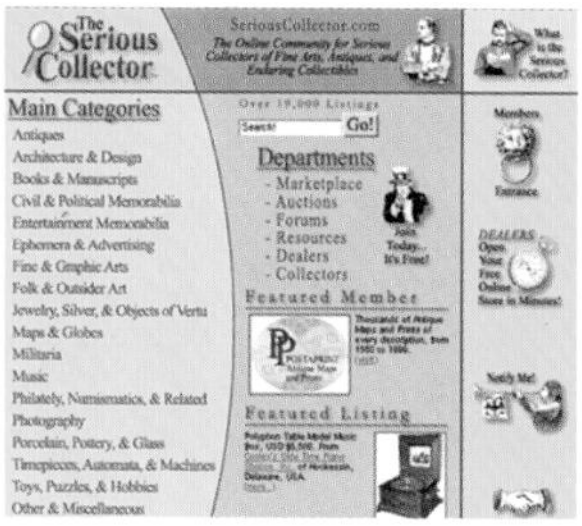

One thing's for sure: you won't find any mangy, bottom-of-the-toy-box *Starsky and Hutch* dolls here. A "gated" online community, The Serious Collector makes it a practice to review each piece of merchandise before it goes on the auction block. Consequently, the quality of goods is much better than at other sites we could mention (but won't). Civil War pistols, Tiffany lamps, Pairpoint candlesticks...they're all here for the buying. Serious fun!

Nicklebys.com www.nicklebys.com
Forget eBay: if you're looking for Warhol watercolors or Phoenician clay flasks, Nicklebys.com is your best bet. Browse auction rooms for the latest antiques, sculpture, and contemporary art works on the market. What's here ain't cheap, but it's bound to satisfy the discriminating collector.

MisterArt.com www.misterart.com
Art supplies for the starving but wired artist. MisterArt.com's selection of discount arts and crafts supplies includes paint, canvases, ceramics, and stuff for kids. Easy pull-down menus, keyword and phonetic searches, and a personalized favorites feature make it easy to find what you need. Be aware, though, that MisterArt.com charges a 15% restocking fee on returned merchandise.

PaintingsDirect.com www.paintingsdirect.com
Yeah, yeah, yeah, we've all heard of Picasso, Renoir, and Manet. But what about Katja Guggenheim and David Curcio? PaintingsDirect.com lets you browse and buy works from promising art world up-and-comers. Once the painting arrives, you have ten days to decide whether or not you like it (return shipping is free). With a little luck, Sotheby's will be knocking on your door in no time.

Atelier America www.atelieramerica.com
If you've always wanted a Van Gogh but haven't managed to scrape up the necessary $1.5 million, skip on over to Atelier America, where you can buy skillful reproductions of oil paintings by the greats. Beware, however: if you don't like what you've bought, you can only get a replacement, exchange, or store credit—refunds are not an option. Choose with care!

ArtSelect www.artselect.com
Feeling enigmatic, romantic, or rustic? If you don't know what artist best suits your walls, ArtSelect lets you search by mood. Once you've found the right print, save it in a Personal Gallery to view later (or run it by your roommate for approval). Get handy tips on color harmony and fixing up challenging spaces at the Design Solutions link.

The Museum Company
www.museumcompany.com
Reproduction decorative objects and gifts from the world's greatest museums, including the British Museum and the Victoria and Albert. Shop The Museum Company for jewelry, stationery, sculpture, nostalgia items, and unique toys. The best selection by far is in home decor—we love the Tiffany lamps and the Frank Lloyd Wright stained glass.

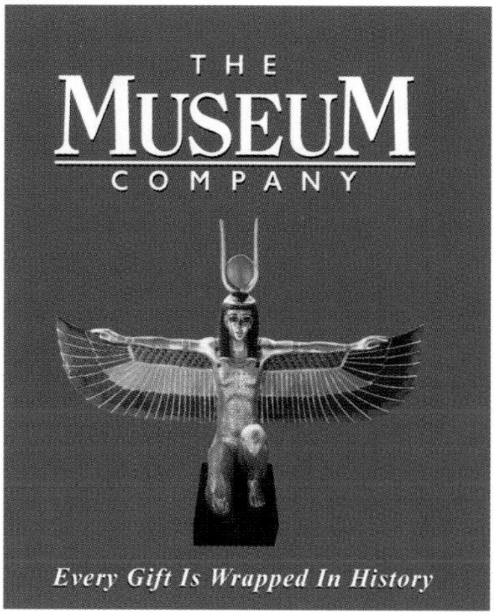

Entertainment Earth
www.entertainmentearth.com
You want *Star Wars*? We've got your *Star Wars* right here! Get your hands on that hard-to-find latex Yoda puppet, pick a Darth Maul mask for Halloween, or preorder hot items months in advance. Entertainment Earth is also a great source for other movie collectibles, including an *X Files* alien mask and a talking *Austin Powers* doll. May the Force be with your credit card.

GUILD.com www.guild.com (d)

Impressionist oils and Edwardian antiques leave you cold? Stop by GUILD.com for decidedly modern sculpture, glass, jewelry, paintings, and more from independent artists—a must for arty living rooms. The chaise lounges here look like they were created with form rather than function in mind, but nobody said art has to be comfortable!

American Frame www.americanframe.com

The range of frames here is impressive—from do-it-yourself kits to ready-made frames to custom-cut sets complete with frame, mat board, and glass. Finding the frame you want takes a little digging, but the price and selection make it worth the click-throughs. Check the tips section for advice on what frames will work best with your decor.

Guggenheim www.guggenheim.org (d)

Frequent-flyer miles be damned. Now you can shop online for beautiful, cutting-edge pieces from the Guggenheim's New York, Bilbao, and Venice shops. Buy a Brancusi replica, a Rauschenberg umbrella, or a scale model of one of Frank Lloyd Wright's masterful designs. Nothing beats going there in person, but this site comes close.

Metropolitan Museum of Art Store
www.metmuseum.org (c) (d) (s)

Exquisite gifts for discriminating tastes. The Met Museum's shop carries fine art books, sculpture, accessories, jewelry, prints, stationery and more. Don't be deterred by the more expensive items here; there are plenty of affordable selections. Should you have any questions, a 24-hour toll-free number is available.

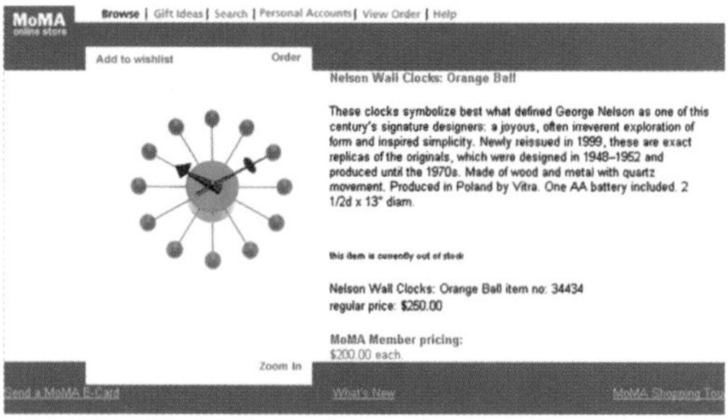

The MoMA Online Store
www.momastore.org (s)

Are you bewitched by Bauhaus or captivated by constructivism? Take a piece of your favorite movement home, courtesy of The MoMA Online Store. Snap up a chaise designed by Le Corbusier, purchase one of Ishiyama's prized pins, or find a hip gift for an art-conscious friend. Museum members get 10% savings (said chaise for $2,061 vs. $2,290), so if you're decking out your house, it's worth it to join.

artnet.com www.artnet.com (c)

Artists and art lovers alike won't want to miss artnet.com. There is a huge selection of prints for sale here, from names like Francis Bacon, David Hockney, and Christo. You can also get online peeks into more than 800 galleries around the world and browse through thousands of artists' portfolios. Well-organized and endlessly inspiring.

NextMonet.com www.nextmonet.com

Todd McKie
A Room of Their Own
12" x 12"
Flashe on paper
1999
$1500

Want to find out what's up in the art world? NextMonet.com will bring you up to speed with an amazing learning tool that breaks down new art by medium, style, characteristic (like color and balance), and subject, decoding each aspect in basic, clear language. After five minutes of surfing, you'll be ready to search their broad range of works to find the perfect asymmetrical still life for your dining room.

Art.com www.art.com

If you've ever known the horror of being buried under an avalanche of Anne Geddes while flipping through a rack of posters, you'll value a site like Art.com. The site's Poster and Print Finder lets you search its stockpile of prints, posters, and photographs by so many different criteria, you're guaranteed to find one you love. Once you make a selection, get framing suggestions at the frame shop or store it in the My Gallery area to show to friends later. Free print for first-time buyers.

Global Gallery www.globalgallery.com

A mountain of Monet, Mondrian, and Miró awaits at Global Gallery, a cool online shop for classic art prints. Pick out a picture, then peruse the artist's bio—when someone asks about your print, you can quip, "Well, Mondrian called it Neo-Plasticism, but I just call it fabulous." If you're a true art novice, be sure to browse the Greatest Works Ever, an illustrated buffet of timeless classics.

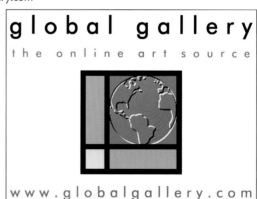

The Warhol Store Online www.warholstore.com

Andy didn't live to see the Internet—he did, however, live to turn the famous mugs of Marilyn, Di, and Elvis into 20th century icons. Pick up these legendary pictures, plus T-shirts, music, clothing, posters, and pasta at The Warhol Store Online. Of course, photographs of Warhol and friends are on view as well.

Auctions & Name Your Price

AuctionRover.com www.auctionrover.com
Why waste precious time scouring site after site for the latest Beanie Baby when you can use AuctionRover.com? Simply enter the object of your desire into the search feature and get a list of auctions that are offering that item. Check out Trend Watch for detailed price histories of more than 300 popular items, including Barbies, Pokémon, and Furbies.

eBay www.ebay.com Ⓒ Ⓢ
Hold on to your wallet. Aside from the usual barrage of collectibles, eBay lets you bid on Ginsu knives, secret lasagna recipes, power drills, and even—get this—a new best friend. You must see it to believe it. Not sure how auctions work? There's a thorough how-to section here that'll start you off right. EBay even offers insurance (up to $200) on items for sale, but we're not sure whether the policy will cover you if that new best friend ditches you.

auctions.com www.auctions.com Ⓢ
If concerns about being duped have kept you away from online auctions, take a look at auctions.com. Their BidSafe program aims to eliminate uncertainty by acting as a middleman to ensure that both buyer and seller are satisfied with the transaction. Sign up for BidSafe and get a 1% rebate to use toward future purchases. Ideal for testing the water in the auction pool.

Yahoo! Auctions auctions.yahoo.com Ⓒ
Yes, Yahoo! does have an auction, and (surprise) it is massive. You'll be astounded by the variety of stuff you can bid on here, everything from global positioning systems to junk mail. Yahoo! absolves itself of any and all responsibility for what's being bought and sold, so don't expect to have your hand held if something goes wrong.

First Auction www.firstauction.com Ⓢ
Find a cheap, fabulous birthday present in the time it takes to watch a *Seinfeld* rerun. First Auction's Flash Auctions take only 30 minutes from start to finish; our visit turned up flatbed scanners, sleeping bags, and a 14K pearl ring. Another intriguing feature: overtime bidding. Even if the auction is over, active bidders can continue to place bids until no one has bid for five minutes. Go ahead—battle it out with other bidders for Kramer's haircomb.

Up4Sale www.up4sale.com
Curly blond hair, a cleft chin, and a happenin' fashion sense—Up4Sale's animated guide, Auction Arnie, is just one difference between Up4Sale and eBay, its parent site. Up4Sale's also got a Tip of the Day link with advice from fellow auction surfers, a member rating system that boots users with low ratings, and a library of related links. Users who register using an anonymous e-mail account (from Hotmail, Yahoo!, or the like) are required to register a credit card number with the site, making auctions here that much more trustworthy.

uBid www.ubid.com

If only shopping at your neighborhood department store were this easy. Like First Auction, uBid doesn't deal with individual sellers, but rather with established vendors. Pros: Because you're dealing directly through uBid, you get better customer service and brand-name products (such as Compaq, Timex, and Calvin Klein). Cons: You won't find the weird, one-of-a-kind items that make browsing the auctions a blast.

Amazon.com LiveBid Auctions www.livebid.com

Going once, going twice, sold to the lady in the back! At Amazon.com LiveBid Auctions, a live video and audio feed lures you into the auction action. Simply register, select an event, and download RealPlayer to get in on the fun. Events are sponsored by respected galleries and auction houses from all over the U.S. The coolest thing auctioned here so far? The original Batmobile from *Batman Returns*, sold for $201,000. Holy simoleans!

Edeal www.edeal.com

Where person-to-person auctions are concerned, it's a Beanie-eat-Beanie world. So it's nice to know you have options like Edeal, an auction site that emphasizes superb customer service for buyers and sellers alike. The site functions as a helpful mediator, collecting payment from buyers and holding onto it until they receive their purchases. The My Control Center link makes it easy to keep tabs on active bids or items on sale. You might get used to feeling this secure.

Popula www.popula.com

The self-dubbed "auction with soul," Popula is a tiny auction site with funky collectibles, antiques, vintage clothing, and housewares. Pick up a pink glitter Astroturf handbag or a 10-piece cow tea set, but bid at your own risk. Popula makes no guarantee about the quality of items for sale and the site is so nicely designed that even the ugliest items might start to look good.

QXL.com www.qxl.com

The ancient Romans used auctions to sell booty seized from defeated rivals. If you have a mind to buy or sell, get your booty to QXL.com, the first name (or rather, initials) in online auctions in Europe. The site has a wide range of standards like computers, electronics, entertainment, and home furnishings, as well as donated items to raise money for charities. For a truly Roman experience, hit the travel and leisure auctions, where you might find a plane ticket to the Eternal City.

Sotheby's www.sothebys.com

While $150,000 may not buy as much as it used to, it will get you a rather nice two-thousand-year-old Egyptian bust. For antiquities, jewelry, sculpture, and paintings, Sotheby's reigns supreme—drop in here for a peek at all the gorgeous stuff and read the entire text from catalogs present and past. To actually buy, you'll need to go to the affiliated sothebys.amazon.com, but this site will help you prepare before you go.

Christie's www.christies.com
IPO millionaires take heed: along with the traditional variety of art and antiques, Christie's also hawks wine, cars, real estate, and sunken cargo, past examples of which can be gawked at online (though you can't view the current catalog). Other online features include buying and selling guides, auction news, a calendar of events, and an easy subscription to LotFinder, a service that searches upcoming auctions for that Toulouse-Lautrec lithograph you can't live without.

i-Escrow www.iescrow.com
E-commerce has brought about a whole new way of doing business. Now folks are willing to plunk down money for items sight unseen to merchants they'll never meet. If you're hesitant to do business this way, then head to i-Escrow. The site provides a neutral place for buyers and sellers to send money and merchandise; when both parties agree that their demands have been fulfilled, i-Escrow sends on the goods. There's a small fee involved, but it may be worth the peace of mind.

i-Escrow®

TradeSafe www.tradesafe.com
Another escrow service to ease your online shopping experience. At TradeSafe, fees are determined by a sliding scale that's based on an item's purchase price and shipping costs; use the handy transaction calculator to determine what percentage each party should pay. TradeSafe deserves kudos for a clear, well-organized FAQ page and a toll-free customer service number. This site also welcomes international business, as long as transactions are conducted in U.S. dollars.

Respond.com www.respond.com
Wrestle with this shopping quandary: it's nearly Halloween and you need a clown costume for your basset hound. Where do you start looking? Try Respond.com. Give them a description of the item you seek, your e-mail address, and a deadline, and the site will e-mail you responses from sellers who have the goods. But take note: anyone who wants to pay the monthly fee can call themselves a seller, and Respond.com isn't going to help you out if that clown wig doesn't fit little Poochie.

Priceline www.priceline.com
One of the few too-good-to-be-true sites that actually is. The site that made "name your price" a reality just keeps getting bigger—these days you can shop Priceline for airline tickets, hotel rooms, groceries, cars, and more. As always, you enter a bid, and Priceline notifies you within an hour if it's a go. While you may have to be flexible about brands, flight times, and the like, it's usually worth it for the money you can save.

imandi.com www.imandi.com
"Imandi" comes from the Hindi word for marketplace, but this site is more about major purchases than everyday buys. Enter a request and get e-mailed competitive quotes on items and services like house painting, an antique couch, a diamond pendant, or a ride to the airport. Imandi.com is free to both buyers and sellers, and while the site won't step in if you get duped, having less phone tag in your life is a definite plus.

myGeek.com www.mygeek.com
If you're the kind of shopper who knows exactly what you want, get thee to myGeek.com. The site will forward your detailed request for ordinary items like an orange juicer, a DVD player, or a case of granola bars to various merchants who then compete for your business. MyGeek.com really cuts out the hassle of comparison surfing for common products; easy-to-follow instructions will zip you through the somewhat complicated process.

eWanted.com www.ewanted.com
Turn the auction upside down! At eWanted.com, buyers post what they're looking for and sellers compete for their business. So a buyer who posts an ad for a small cappuccino machine for under $50 will receive bids from people who are willing to sell the product at that price. The buyer simply picks from the descriptions or pictures he or she has been sent and contacts that seller. A great way to get deep discounts on everything from art to airplane parts—without the effort of visiting the auctions.

NexTag.com www.nextag.com
Hate paying retail? Then skip on over to NexTag.com, where you name the price you want to pay for computer software and hardware. If a vendor accepts your bid, you must buy or suffer the consequences (namely, getting a bad reputation at this Web site). The service is free and, unlike an auction site, sales can be closed within minutes. Works best for informed consumers who know exactly what they want and how much they want to spend.

Hagglezone.com www.hagglezone.com
Are you a compulsive bargainer? Hagglezone.com lets you name your price on electronics, cameras, knives, outdoor equipment, and whatever else they can find. They have six "haggler" personalities with whom you bargain, and the price depends in part on which one you pick. Sound confusing? It is, but it's fun to try. You're never obligated to buy just because you offer a price, so it's worth playing around to see what you can get.

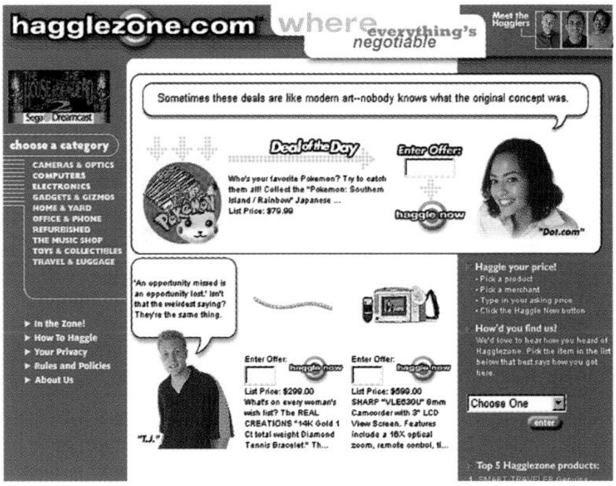

Accompany www.accompany.com
Accompany's got an unusual sales strategy that relies on bulk purchasing to get low prices for customers. Click to buy a Palm Pilot, for example, and you join the Buy-Cycle for that item. As more people join the group, the price of that Palm Pilot keeps on dropping. When the Buy-Cycle closes, you'll be notified via e-mail of the closing price you secured with the help of your team members. Of course, it works to your advantage to get family, friends, and coworkers to join up. Just be careful: once you click the Buy button, you're committed to purchasing the item.

Baby & Maternity

iBaby.com www.ibaby.com (s)
iBaby.com's got all the equipment and baby supplies a mom could want, from strollers and car seats to bassinets and breast pumps. While you're there, be sure to check out fun and informative features like the Baby Name Finder and the New Parent Checklist, which lists all the must-have stuff for your precious one.

BabyCenter.com www.babycenter.com (s)
Whether you're considering taking the big plunge into parenthood or already have a playpen full of li'l nippers, BabyCenter.com can help you navigate the exhausting—er, uplifting—road of parenthood. The site has tips on everything from when to conceive to disciplining toddlers to starting a college fund. Once you've got the basics down, head to the store for fabulous products designed to distract parents from their nonexistent sex lives.

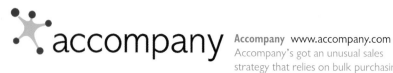

babystyle.com
www.babystyle.com (d)
For little ones whose first word was "DKNY," babystyle.com's got chic clothes (maternity, too!) from designers like Zutano, Hanna Andersson, and DKNYBaby. After you've maxed out your credit card, be sure to check out such features as Cindy's Corner, where supermodel Crawford shares her thoughts on "style, stardom, and the joys of bringing up baby."

BabyGifts.com www.babygifts.com
If you don't know Zwiebacks from Cushie-Tushies, chances are you could use some help come next baby shower. Search BabyGifts.com by price, age, or brand to find presents that a parent can really use—including essential home safety items like power strip covers and stair gates. Other great options: toy boxes, step stools, and growth charts that you can personalize with the baby's name.

Belly Basics www.nystyle.com/bellyb
A simple, classic line with a celebrity following, Belly Basics offers a Pregnancy Survival Kit that makes maternity dressing a snap. The kit includes four indispensable black wardrobe basics designed with comfort and quality in mind (no elastic waistbands!). If only they made clothes for the rest of us: how about a travel wardrobe in a box? Or a college wardrobe in a box?

Anna Cris Maternity www.annacris.com ⓢ
Sick of clothes that make you look like a lumpy pup tent? Anna Cris' collection of maternity apparel is classic, current, and decidedly non-tentlike. The online selection includes smart casuals to last even after the nine months are up, plus comfy weekend pieces, belly-compatible undies, and fitness clothes. The best part? Anna Cris pays for shipping on returns.

iMaternity.com www.imaternity.com ⓢ
Calling all prospective moms: the folks at iMaternity.com have been there and are happy to do your maternity shopping for you. Sit back, relax, and shop for basics, suits, lingerie, and even jeans without leaving your chair. (Your back will thank you!) The selection and service are stellar. Be sure to check out the site's sizing chart, which helps you figure out your new size.

iVillage
iMaternity.com
the maternity everything store

Bath & Beauty

eve · com
the beauty of the internet

eve.com www.eve.com ⓒ ⓓ
Eve may have felled Adam without lipstick and concealer, but face it, ladies: times have changed. Eve.com is a one-stop beauty shop for products to keep you looking and smelling your best, whatever garden you may wander into. The site deserves kudos for offering brands like BeneFit and Tony & Tina, a beauty advice hotline, and pull-down menus that let you search for advice by beauty flaw (acne to stretch marks).

ibeauty.com www.ibeauty.com ⓒ ⓢ

Finally! Learn the difference between ultra-rich and ultra-long lashes, and compare the benefits of shiatsu and Swedish massage. In addition to the big names in makeup (Lancôme, Clinique, Philosophy), ibeauty.com offers a unique beauty guide that helps you locate a hair dresser, masseuse, or plastic surgeon in your area. It even provides a glossary of terms so you can discuss rhinoplasty and dermabrasion with confidence. If you're unsure of a new fragrance or color, ibeauty's local directory resource will put you in touch with a department store in your neighborhood where you can try on your online selections. A fantastic resource.

SmashBox www.smashbox.com ⓓ

Quality over quantity is the approach at SmashBox, a makeup line designed by makeup artists and fashion designers. The site focuses on a few carefully developed products like anti-shine lipstick and cream eyeliner, in a choice selection of shades rather than hundreds of different colors. Free shipping for orders over $50 takes the edge off the prices, so go ahead and splurge.

sephora.com www.sephora.com

Sephora's much-hyped site offers indulgence at every turn, with tons of makeup and fragrances, professional tools, and bath accessories. Designed in sleek black with beauty advice from the likes of François Nars and Vincent Longo, the site attempts to recreate the luxe and sparkle of its real-life stores, with mixed results. (Why the ingredient lists? Who really cares that Hard Candy Disco 2000 contains talc, silica, and epoxy resin-coated polyethylene?) For makeup purists, though, the site's superior selection redeems.

Clinique www.clinique.com ⓒ

When you absolutely, positively cannot live with combination skin another day, head for Clinique. With beauty articles, a color and skin-type calculator, and an extensive selection of advice and products for men and women, the site brings you all the benefits of the beauty counter and then some.

BeautyBuys.com www.beautybuys.com

Who says beauty products have to be expensive? BeautyBuys.com offers discounts on cosmetics, fragrances, and hair care products; this is the place to check first for expensive brands like Aveda and La Prairie. The site looks a little like the coupon circulars you get in the newspaper, but with good selection and prices—and free UPS shipping on orders of $60 or more—who cares?

Urban Decay www.urbandecay.com

With makeup inspired by "the beautiful hues of our urban landscape," Urban Decay will hook you up with some Spare Change nail enamel, Stalker eye shadow, or Uzi lipstick in the blink of a mascara-laden eye. Sure, your choices may not win favor with dear old Mom (unless mater happens to be Patti Smith), but they're destined to stop traffic. Check out the Apply It feature to avoid achieving the trashy look when you were really going for slutty.

Perfumania.com www.perfumania.com
Wary about buying fragrances online? This clicks-and-mortar retailer carries well-known brands at surprisingly discounted prices. Choose from Chanel, Charlie, Polo, and others, or experiment with aromatherapy oils and kids' scents. The store locator will help you find a Perfumania in your area if you'd like to sample a scent first.

Jasmin.com www.jasmin.com (c)
At Jasmin.com, hundreds of designer scents for men and women are browsable by name, fragrance family (Fresh, Oriental, Floriental, etc.), designer, and country of origin—a boon for hard-core fragrance fans. There's also a unique bottles section, a perfume museum, and an interesting history that goes all the way back to the blue waterlily perfume of ancient Egypt. (Where can we score some of that?)

gloss.com www.gloss.com (d)
Forget Cover Girl and Maybelline—gloss.com's got Bloom, Blue Q, Get Fresh, FaceStation, and other hard-to-find face savers recommended in the fashion pages. A little like a magazine and makeup counter rolled into one, gloss.com covers celebrity makeup trends and gives detailed primers on how to get the face of the moment. Want Winona Ryder's lips? Gwyneth Paltrow's eyes? You're at the right place.

Crabtree & Evelyn www.crabtree-evelyn.com
Designed for those moments when you need to feel like everything's in sync, from your home decor to your bath salts. Crabtree & Evelyn offers lotions, soaps, fragrances, and a carefully culled selection of teas, cookies, and preserves. Need a quick gift? The site offers gift basket ideas, free gift-wrapping, and optional Express Mail next-day service.

Bobbi Brown Cosmetics www.bobbibrowncosmetics.com (c)
Bobbi Brown is a real woman who knows it's hard to look collected when juggling a hectic life (cosmetic company, three kids, new book). Lucky for us, her makeup is designed to go from the boardroom to the bedroom and back. The awesome video tutorial here takes the guess-work out of application techniques, and beauty tips for African American, Asian, and Latina women are a breath of fresh air.

Avon shop.avon.com
Everything Avon (which is more than you think), all in one place. Search here for products geared toward concealing flaws and enhancing assets: Cellulite Control Gel, Lighten Up Undereye Treatment, and Stress Shield Serum, for starters. For outdoorsy types, there's an awesome moisturizer that doubles as mosquito repellent. Ain't science grand?

philosophy www.philosophy.com
Hair care, makeup, and skin products that are short on chemicals and long on Zen. The philosophy is simple: the site offers clean, fresh-smelling makeup with fanciful product names like Hope in a Jar, Head Trip, and Help Me. And if that Hope in a Jar turns out to be hopeless? Return what you haven't used for a full refund.

beautyscene.com www.beautyscene.com Ⓢ

Beauty may be only skin deep, but a lot rides on that fraction of an inch. Use beautyscene.com's My Kit feature to look calm, collected, and exceptionally cool. My Kit keeps track of the makeup and beauty supplies you frequently buy and sends you a reminder when it's time to reorder. You'll have to become a member to use it, but registering (for free) also gets you free shipping and beauty advice from *Cosmo* founder Helen Gurley Brown.

Beautyhabit www.beautyhabit.com

Recreate the spa experience at home with candles, vitamins, aromatherapy oils, and cosmetics from Beautyhabit. A glimpse of the brand names lets you know you're not in Kansas anymore—Christian Tortu, Maison Jaquet Paris, and Phytokosma line the virtual shelves. If these names mean nothing to you, browsing Beautyhabit will be difficult. Still, if you're burning to try out a fun new product (like eucalyptus dentifrice), you may stumble on something here.

SpaWish.com www.spawish.com

Spread bliss to your gal (or guy) pals care of SpaWish.com. Just type in the recipient's name and address and SpaWish.com will send them a gift certificate in the amount of your choice ($50 minimum), redeemable at any one of 700 national spas. While you're at it, why not sign up for one yourself? You deserve a little pampering!

Books

barnesandnoble.com www.bn.com Ⓒ Ⓢ

Could 2.9 million people in more than 215 countries be wrong? At barnesandnoble.com, the numbers speak for themselves: 750,000 titles in stock, 50% discounts on *New York Times* best-sellers, and 2,800 books under $5. The Out of Print section may be one of their best features: they have millions of used, rare, and out-of-print books in their searchable database.

Borders.com www.borders.com Ⓒ Ⓢ

What's cool about Borders.com? The community. While you may not be able to sip a mochaccino while you're there, the online NetCafe offers staff recommendations, chats with popular authors, and a chance to register your opinions. You'll also find a huge selection of music and videos here (for a total of 10 million books, CDs, and videos), and discounts of 50% on forthcoming books and *New York Times* best-sellers.

BOL.com www.uk.bol.com Ⓒ Ⓢ

What's Europe's answer to the virtual book megastore? BOL.com, aka Bertelsmann Online. The supersite offers a buffet of services for readers to gorge on: search by category, author, title, or ISBN, create a customized profile, or check out gift recommendations, features, and book reviews. Follow the links from BOL.com's home page for book sites in France, Germany, Spain, Switzerland, and the Netherlands.

wordsworth.com www.wordsworth.com Ⓒ

Despise *The Bridges of Madison County*? Gag at the sight of the latest Danielle Steele epi-romance? Then plant your alternative butt before wordsworth.com, "an independent store for independent minds." After loading up your shopping cart with the works of such literary luminaries as Martha Cooley and Chinua Achebe (check the Recommendations for more suggestions), take a crack at the Weekly Contest, which gives prizes for identifying a book based on its first or last line.

A Common Reader www.commonreader.com Ⓒ

Common reading? Hardly. This lovely, intelligent site compiles all the best and most interesting works of literature you've likely never heard of, arranged in categories such as A World of Words, Science and the Secrets of Nature, and The Presence of the Past. Discover titles like *A Pessimist's Guide to History* or *The Poetry of Home*, or delve into ACR's reprints of long-lost works from such writers as Dodie Smith, Angela Thirkell, and Betty MacDonald.

Fatbrain.com www.fatbrain.com Ⓒ Ⓢ

Stuff your head to bursting with science, math, computer, and business books from Fatbrain.com. Their books and manuals, interactive training software, and same day shipping are great for those times when you need to learn SQL, DBS, or C++, fast. Quick-response customer service and extras like the customized corporate bookstore are tops.

Bibliofind www.bibliofind.com Ⓒ Ⓢ

Bibliofind searches dusty library stacks, specialty bookshops, and old magazine racks to bring you rare and out-of-print books and periodicals online. Find your favorite poet in the original French (or Sanskrit), or get a signed copy of Eleanor Roosevelt's memoir. If Bibliofind doesn't carry it, they will seek it out for you. Well-written, loving descriptions make it seem as though they really care about the books—a rarity in our age of warehouse booksellers.

A Different Light www.adlbooks.com

With books, videos, and informational features, A Different Light is a community space as much as a bookstore for the gay, lesbian, bisexual, and transgender communities. The site doesn't have a shopping cart to store items, but ordering is relatively easy and books are shipped promptly and discreetly. It's nice to know that your purchases here support the community in the form of donations, readings, and a forum for new and unpublished writers.

Audio Book Club

Audio Book Club www.audiobookclub.com
Whether you want to "read" while you drive or simply need to drown out the rest of the world, head for the Audio Book Club. They've got loads of titles from authors like John Grisham, Michael Crichton, and Patricia Cornwell that you can preview before you buy. Keep in mind that this is a book club, so you'll have to join to get the goods–buy the first four titles for a cent, and the next two at regular prices (usually under $15 dollars).

Alibris www.alibris.com
For out-of-fashion favorites, turn to Alibris; the site's Book Hound will search out any title that isn't in their impressive collection of out-of-print, rare, or first-edition books. After you've tracked down your grandmother's cookbook or your favorite childhood story, head to the Community Section, where sci-fi fans, mystery addicts, and other bibliophiles opine online.

Cherry Valley Books www.cherryvalleybooks.com
Founded by a mom with a mission to bring high-quality reads online, Cherry Valley Books is a boon for parents who want to wean their kids off MTV and Nintendo. You'll find wonderful children's stories for all age groups here, including classics like *Bridge to Terabithia* and up-and-comers like *The Music of Dolphins*. Search for special themes (Halloween, birthdays) or specific characters (ethnic minorities, girls, children with disabilities). A marvelous store.

1bookstreet.com www.1bookstreet.com
You're no dummy if you buy your next *Idiot's Guide* at 1bookstreet.com; the site offers giant savings on the popular titles you love, including 40% discounts on all of Oprah's picks and free shipping for orders over $15. For some really thought-provoking reading, click through to Ray's Rants, the senior editor's forum for venting on such diverse topics as bad spelling on the Internet and online urban legends.

BIGWORDS.com www.bigwords.com ⓓ
Trust us: you will never, ever need that physics textbook again. Unload the albatross at BIGWORDS.com, a site that is prepared to give you cash or credit for scintillating study aids like *Intermediate Accounting and Calculus: Early Transcendentals*. The inspired search feature allows searching for books by title, author, or professor (for participating schools).

efollet.com www.efollet.com
Whether you're studying P.E. at Walla Walla College or E.E. at Stanford, efollet.com makes it easy to get all your textbooks in one fell swoop. The site has links to more than 800 college e-stores that stock the specific books needed for their courses. Don't worry if your campus isn't online yet; the site can also search by subject, title, author, or ISBN to find it somewhere else.

netLibrary www.netlibrary.com ©

All you need is a (free) netLibrary card, and you're ready to browse, read, and borrow e-books online. The focus here is on how-to, scholarly, and research books from a variety of publishers and university presses. Just like in a real library, only one user at a time can look at a book, and there are strict warnings throughout about copyright infringement. Unlike a real library, however, netLibrary is open 24-7.

Maps.com www.maps.com

Was I supposed to make a right at Santa Fe? Or was that a left at Albuquerque? Admit it: you don't know where you're going, and you need a map. Maps.com has some remarkably innovative maps, globes, and atlases. Buy a traveler's map that shows all the best hiking spots in the Olympic National Forest; download a high-quality digital map for your Web site; or pick up a laminated road map to avoid origami map folding. Maps.com will even customize a map to suit your needs if you're willing to foot the $80 per hour bill.

Enews.com www.enews.com

Are you out of the loop? At Enews.com you can try any popular magazine free for 90 days and then cancel at no charge if you decide not to keep it. Choices run the gamut of mainstream magazines, from *Popular Mechanics* to *Vogue*, *Newsweek*, and *Entertainment Weekly*. Read *Playboy* for the articles? They'll describe the contents of the latest issue before you start your sample subscription.

Bridal

Della Weddings www.dellaweddings.com

From the basic truth that 12 toasters is 11 too many came the wedding registry. Della Weddings offers a cool way to bring all of your registries together in one online interface. Register on the site (or in-store) for gifts from Dillard's, Crate & Barrel, REI, and more than 25 others. Della Weddings will send e-mail to your guests to let them know how to purchase the items online. What could be easier?

Wedding Expressions www.weddingexpressions.com

More than 8,000 square feet of gowns, tuxedos, gifts, and accessories... now online. Looks like marriage is back in fashion! Wedding Expressions is a terrific resource for stressed-out couples planning the ceremony of the century. Pick up all the clothes for the wedding party, plus accessories like personalized chocolates, wedding glitter, bubble blowers, and—for the romantically clueless—a 12-piece honeymoon passion package.

The Knot www.theknot.com ⓒ ⓢ

Advice and products for every aspect of your nuptials from "Will you ...?" to "I do." Choose a gown, pick a ring, register for goodies—then, once you've covered the basics, find a DJ, feather your love nest, and decide on your cake topper. For the finishing touch, don't leave without visiting the Knot Shop for accessories that are both serious (ring pillows) and lighthearted (church-shaped bubbles).

WeddingNetwork.com www.weddingnetwork.com ⓒ

Clever couples know how to budget before they buy. The wedding planner here will help you amass a checklist of pre-ceremony to-dos, schedule wedding events, and figure out how much it's all going to cost your parents. You can also chat live with a bridal consultant, find a local photographer, and read tips from *Modern Bride*. Naturally, there is an extensive registry (100+ retailers), so go ahead and splurge.

WeddingChannel.com www.weddingchannel.com ⓒ

Register at WeddingChannel.com for linens, crystal, and other assorted necessities from respected retailers like Macy's, The Bon Marché, and Stern's. The site will also help you to outfit the flower girls, teach you the difference between a sweep train and a chapel train, and help to navigate ever-touchy bachelor party politics. Who ever thought weddings could be this complicated?

Cars

CarParts.com www.carparts.com ⓢ

Whether you're a real greasemonkey or just hoping to replace a squeaky windshield wiper blade yourself, CarParts.com can make the job a breeze. They have more than 1.5 million parts available (choose from 10 different wiper blades) for almost any car (Pintos to Bentleys). Beginners should read the repair manual (available on the site) for their particular make and model before attempting any major overhauls.

JC Whitney www.jcwhitney.com

Hot accessories to get your car, truck, or SUV into tip-top shape. Shop here for a radar detector, a roof rack, or even a mobile TV and VCR; you don't need to be a car expert to find tons of cool (and gift-worthy) merchandise. After 80 years in the catalog business, the people at JC Whitney know their stuff; sign up for their newsletter, e-Highway, to hear about new product releases, technical tips, and special deals for your car.

CSKAUTO.com www.cskauto.com

Target audience: do-it-yourselfers. CSKAUTO.com has parts for almost any vehicle, tools for every repair job, and a respectable offering of tips and how-tos. Search by manufacturer part number if you know exactly what you need. After you've souped up your old heap of junk, be sure to submit photos to the site; you might earn a place on their Cool Cars page.

Kelley Blue Book www.kbb.com ©

If you've never heard of Kelley Blue Book, you've probably been walking for the last 70 years. First published in 1926, this is still the definitive place to figure out how much your old clunker is worth. Get trade-in and retail prices on used cars, motorcycles, watercraft, and snowmobiles, or check on how much it'd cost you to get the new car you've always wanted. If the thousands upon thousands of car prices don't keep you busy, spend some time reading reviews, searching for a local dealer, or browsing for auto insurance or a loan.

Motorcycle USA www.motorcycleusa.com

We haven't forgotten you two-wheeled motorists! You can't buy a motorcycle here, but you can get everything you need to go with it, from helmets to handlebars, shipped direct from the Portland, Oregon store. The accessories section even features drink systems, so you'll never have to make a pit stop to quench your thirst.

The Tire Rack www.tirerack.com ©

Do you have a spare in your trunk? If not, get thee to The Tire Rack, where you can quickly search for a new set of wheels by tire size or brand. Need help choosing? There are plenty of articles here to assist, plus The Wheel Rack, an interactive guide that lets you see what particular wheels look like on a specific make, model, and year of car.

1-800 Drive Today
www.1-800drivetoday.com

1-800 Drive Today is a very simple site: fill out a brief online car loan application, and you'll hear from a loan specialist whether or not you've been approved. The site specializes in getting loans for clients who have a bad credit history or credit problems, and while the interface itself is low-tech, it's a valuable service if you've got a blemished record.

Car Clicks www.carclicks.com ©

Follow the car-buying roadmap on this site for step-by-step help that takes you from homework to comparison shopping to delivery. A sidebar of links also points you toward sites that will give you important services for free. Get your credit report, compare financing packages, and, of course, run a Lemon Check—enter the car's Vehicle Identification Number to see if any problems have been reported.

CarPrice.com www.carprice.com ©

Don't get taken for a ride—there's a lot more to a car's value than the MSRP. Gas mileage, insurance, and depreciation are all factors, and CarPrice.com's cost calculators can help you see how. The site also offers informational pages on negotiation, price quotes, and warranties, as well as a library of cool links. You can even get help figuring out a car's "target price," the critical but oft-ignored idea of what a car is actually worth, as opposed to what it's priced at.

edmunds.com
consumer driven

Edmunds.com www.edmunds.com ⓒ
The car-buying scenarios on this site read a little like Stephen King (no one said getting inside the head of an auto dealer would be pretty), but if you're in the market to buy a new or used car, you'll find them very informative reading. You'll also find price lists, pros and cons, and warranty information for the makes and models you like. Before you buy, see how a vehicle holds up over time with the Long Term Road Tests, or find out how similar models match up using the Comparison Tests section.

The IntelliChoice Car Center www.intellichoice.com
The costs behind a car's sticker price can be more mysterious than the ingredients in a Christmas fruitcake. Use the IntelliChoice Window Sticker program to unravel the mystery: simply choose a car, tack on the options one by one, and watch the price climb. Still unsure if you're getting your money's worth? Stop by the BOV (Best Overall Value) awards page to see which of last year's selection made the grade.

CarScene.com www.carscene.com
You may not be able to get Reggie Jackson's swing, but if you've got $25,000, you can have his pink Coupe DeVille. CarScene.com has listings for the auto connoisseur, from one-of-a-kind antiques to souped-up muscle cars. Some are for sale through classifieds, others are being auctioned; go ahead and click on your dream car to get the contact info. Even if you're not buying, check out the pictures of rare and special interest cars—the celebrity section lists Tammy Wynette's Cougar convertible and Bill Cosby's Mercedes Benz.

Autobytel.com www.autobytel.com ⓒ
At Autobytel.com, you can choose a car like you would a Denny's entree: simply browse the pictures for the most appetizing one and point. The site has a virtual photo album that shows hundreds of makes and models of new cars. Click on the one you like, and you'll get detailed pricing info and a 360-degree interactive view of the interior. A selection of used cars (also with pictures!) is available in the Certified Pre-Owned Cyberstore.

InvoiceDealers.com www.invoicedealers.com
Many car sites leave you to cool your heels for a day while they process your quote request. Not InvoiceDealers.com. This site's one and only purpose is immediate price quotes, flashed on the screen seconds after you enter the make, model, and options package (no need to wait for an e-mail). They give you the dealers' contact information as well, in case you're ready to move forward with a purchase or have some questions.

CarSmart.com www.carsmart.com ⓒ
Did you know that a Saturday in late November is the best time to buy a car? CarSmart.com's Auto Advisor provides insider hints to give you a leg up when car shopping. You'll also like the Express Quote feature—tell them what new car you've been eyeing; they'll get you a bona fide quote from one of their hundreds of affiliated dealerships in 24 hours or less. You're not obligated to take the offer, but it does give you a haggle-free starting point. Additional offerings include classifieds, consumer guides, test drives, and sneak previews of funky futuristic cars.

AutoTrader.com www.autotrader.com ⓒ

Which cars come equipped with your must-have features? Use AutoTrader.com's Decision Guide to find out. Program in the options you want (driver's-side air bag, hatchback, extra leg room, etc.), and the site lists models that match your criteria, complete with an exhaustive breakdown on each. Once you know what you want, take advantage of the site's used car locator—with 1.5 million listings, you're sure to find several for sale near you.

cars.com www.cars.com ⓒ

Cars.com has a handy car finder for both new and used cars: just type in the make/model, a price range, and your zip code, and the site will tell you which dealers in your area are selling it. Be sure to check the site's e-store for a list of current dealer rebates (as well as the usual links for financing, insurance, parts, and accessories). Bookmark-worthy bonus: the unfailingly funny Car Talk section, with random surveys (Jeep drivers think they're taller than most), and a Car-O-Scope that tells you if your vehicle matches your personality.

carOrder.com www.carorder.com ⓒ ⓓ

The Texas-based company is taking auto e-tailing into new territory by buying brick-and-mortar dealerships around the country. But for now, the site is (like other car-buying sites) a middleman that lets you customize your car online, then orders the car for you directly from the manufacturer. A $500 deposit is required. The best feature here is the ability to customize your car exactly to your specifications—the clean, intuitive interface makes it simple. Then click for a quote, type in your credit card number, and carOrder.com will have your new wheels delivered, complete with a big red bow. What could be more convenient?

CarsDirect.com www.carsdirect.com ⓒ ⓢ

CarsDirect.com is a perfect example of how the Internet can both empower consumers and make their lives a whole lot easier. This simple but clever service takes you step by step through the process of choosing a car, getting a financing or leasing deal, and ordering your vehicle. All orders come with free roadside assistance for the next six years. We'll withhold our praise until the site can cook us dinner, though.

AutoSite www.autosite.com
Whether you're looking for a sedan for your family or a convertible for your midlife crisis, the info-packed AutoSite has price lists, spec reports, options information, and details down to the last nut and bolt. Once you know what you want, read through their financing and insurance information, and then use their streamlined classifieds interface to find your new set of wheels.

LeaseSource Online www.leasesource.com ©
Found the car you want? LeaseSource Online will help you figure out how to pay for it. Everything is here to help you make sense of the financials: first, use the lease profiler to determine whether you should lease or buy. Then visit the leasing classroom for basic information and Q&A. If leasing is right for you, the site's Matchmaker section can connect you with a lessor in your area.

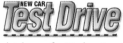

New Car Test Drive www.nctd.com ©
NEW CAR Test Drive
Don't put your trust in a slick-talking, hairgel-dripping, white loafer-wearing car salesman when you can access this site's database of critical write-ups. The New Car Test Drive team has checked out models issued from 1994 to 2001, and their reviews and comments should help you get a feel for the car you're thinking of buying. Did you know that if you're going 75 mph in a 2000 Pontiac Montana, the speedometer needle blocks the turn indicator light? You would if you'd read the review.

Catalogs

Catalog City www.catalogcity.com
Shop online from more than 200 catalogs, ranging from the familiar (Neiman Marcus, Lane Bryant) to the obscure (Acme Lite Laser Pointers, ADD-IT Fertilizer Injectors). Or have a print catalog delivered to your home (choose from 13,000 possibilities). The easy-to-use search page here offers a good range of options, and the sheer volume of products available is mind-boggling. You'll have to go to the individual catalog merchants for shipping, returns, and other customer service information.

The Catalog Site www.catalogsite.com

The mere thought of The Catalog Site is enough to make normally docile mail carriers go postal, but you'll love how easy it is to order the 200+ catalogs available here. There are the popular perennials like JCrew and Gump's, plus lesser-known organizations (Blossom Flower Shop, Scent Warehouse, and SelfCare). Better buy a bigger mailbox.

Catalog.com www.catalog.com

Catalog.com scours catalogs and Web sites for the coolest merch and plunks it down right at your virtual feet. "Communities" like Animal Lovers, Auto Enthusiasts, and Gen X allow interest-specific browsing, though a search engine is also available. Be sure to check for a lock icon as you browse the store listings—Catalog.com marks the sites that are known to have secure ordering.

Classifieds

Excite Classifieds classifieds.excite.com ⓒ ⓓ

Searching for a lonely SWF or a kickin' SUV? Your first stop should be Excite Classifieds. Sign up for a member name and password and ads are free to search and free to post—the 2.3 million listings should keep you busy for a while. If you can't find what you seek, sign up for Cool Notify and the site will e-mail you when an ad appears with what you're looking for.

Classified Warehouse.com www.classifiedwarehouse.com ⓒ

Though the idea of being hounded by a classifieds site does give us pause, AdHound does the right kind of dogging. It sifts through classified listings specific to your area and e-mails you when it thinks it's found what you want. If you'd rather browse ads yourself, the site will also let you "clip" listings for later reading. Just like in normal newspapers, you'll need to watch out for hidden corporate ads, and avoid the lame Lost and Found section—that is, unless you like reading three postings on the same missing dachshund.

Loot www.loot.com ⓒ

Bursting with ads and auctions, there's something for everyone at Loot, the United Kingdom's classified source. Dedicated bargain-hunters will love the Loot Café, which provides tips on where to find money-saving deals online. The selection here is better for folks looking for merchandise than jobs or dates.

Epage www.ep.com

Attention sellers: Epage's unique feedback system lets you post classified ads without releasing your e-mail address, so you don't have to worry about being deluged with spam. Buyers should check out the site's Popular Ads link to see which ads everyone else likes. The selection here is highly variable, and some of the personals can get rather racy; squeamish surfers should take care.

Clothing & Accessories

Bluefly.com www.bluefly.com
ⓒ ⓓ ⓢ
Everyone's buzzing about Bluefly.com these days, and for once, the hype is deserved. Three reasons why you must visit: top designers (Cynthia Rowley, Prada, and Calvin Klein), deep discounts (50% off on a Daryl K dress), and a 90-day return policy. Click on Flypaper for the latest news from the fashion world, or poke through their housewares if you have a small space to deck out.

L.L.Bean www.llbean.com ⓒ
Sporty casuals for men, women, and kids are the best reason to shop L.L.Bean, but there are other cool features on the site: you can read expert advice on outdoor sports or search for detailed information on any one of 1,800 state and national parks. The handy catalog quickshop option makes ordering almost instantaneous; for those without a catalog, browsing through the product guides is a breeze.

Girlshop www.girlshop.com
Oodles and oodles of fabulous clothes. You could shop with your eyes closed and still find something cool at Girlshop, where you'll have access to tiny, cutting-edge collections (under a dozen pieces) from more than 30 designers, including Candy Barr, Noir NYC, and Wang. Flip from boutique to boutique to find clothes you won't see anywhere else, or register a wish list to guarantee stylish birthday presents.

boo.com www.boo.com ⓓ ⓢ
Say bye-bye to 2-D shopping and just boo it. Boo.com's site is even more dynamic than its kickin' sports- and streetwear. Pick a shirt or a pair of pants and then spin them around, zoom in for details, or see how they look with other items. Can't decide? Consult the fab Miss Boo, an animated shopping assistant who winks, blinks, and offers cheeky advice. Free shipping, free returns, lots of fun.

Newport News www.newport-news.com
Breezy, go-anywhere clothes for women at fantastic prices. (How does $16 for a pair of jeans sound?) Whether you're looking for casual sportswear or something dressy for the office, you'll find it here, and you may even find it in petite or tall sizes. There's also a bed and bath section with handsome comforters, slipcovers, curtains, and towels. The one hitch? Telephone customer service inquiries will cost you.

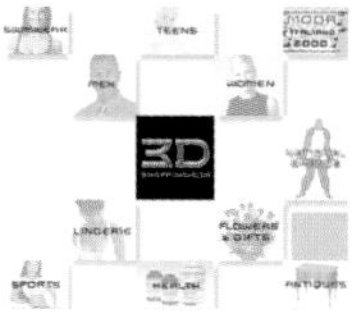

3DShopping.com www.3dshopping.com
Swimwear, lingerie, clothing, sportswear, and even antiques—3DShopping.com is a unique site that understands the importance of actually seeing the merchandise up-close, from every angle. 3D may be stretching it, but expect to find somewhere in the neighborhood of 360-degree views of clothing for men, women, and teens; close-ups on clothing details (like patterns, sequins, and color swatches) are also a plus. The brands are as-yet unknown, but there are some finds to be had here.

Outletmall.com www.outletmall.com
Adidas, Esprit, DKNY, Prada, and 50 more top designers at rock-bottom prices will make you want to, like, hit the mall (so to speak). The selection at Outletmall.com is slim, but the site is worth a browse for deals on men's and women's clothing and home accessories. Check in often, as products are available in limited quantities only.

Northwest Express www.northwestexpress.com (s)
Shetland wool, cotton knits, silk angora: if you seek casual comfort with Northwest flair, you'll find it at Northwest Express. From Harry & David (the food retailer) come these comfy clothes, decorative wares, and garden supplies, plus an online auction where you can name your price on overstocked items. If you order from the site, be sure to let Northwest Express know if you don't want to be on their mailing list; the easy-to-understand privacy policy tells you how.

American Eagle Outfitters www.ae.com
The mall favorite is online with a limited selection of outdoorsy casuals. Check in at American Eagle Outfitters for men's and women's sweaters, fleeces, jeans, and outerwear. Nearly everything is under $40.

jcrew.com www.jcrew.com (d)
Think about it: Who doesn't have a JCrew sweater tucked somewhere in their closet? The store-cum-catalog of cool and classy basics is online (of course) and totally simple to use. Why bother with the Web? Incentives include weekly sales (often at 50% discounts), a clearance link, and for those with the catalog, direct ordering by product number.

The Wasteland www.thewasteland.com
Vintage clothing hounds rejoice: The Wasteland is online. The store that's synonymous with second-hand chic will have you decked out in rare retro gear faster than you can say polyester blend. The clear pictures, intuitive design, and a carefully chosen selection will make you wonder why you ever rummaged through mothy clothing bins at the local Goodwill.

Brandmania.com www.brandmania.com
With a name like Brandmania.com, it's not surprising that there's an undercurrent of mental instability running through this discount clothing site ("Insane deals!" "Save like crazy!"). But with sales of up to 70% off suggested retail and free shipping, we can withstand the used-car sales tactics. Outfit your whole family, then proceed to the housewares section for accessories like sheets, towels, and candles. While the selection is random at best, what's here is worth picking through.

Blue ASPHALT.COM

Blue Asphalt www.blueasphalt.com (d)
If online shopping has you pining for a trip to the mall with your best friend, you've just found the remedy. Browse Blue Asphalt's shirts, pants, and frilly girlie dresses, and then head to the virtual changing room to check out how stuff actually looks. If you can't get a friend to shop with you, visit "Phoebe," a hilarious and spunky online animation who will keep you company and let you hang out in her room.

Becoming, Inc. www.becoming.com
Believe it: one out of nine women has breast cancer. Where can they shop? Becoming, Inc. Each dress, jacket, swimsuit, and bra available here was designed to fit the comfort and style needs of women living with breast cancer. Bonus: Becoming, Inc. donates 2% of its profits to breast cancer research and offers links to cancer-related sites.

bargainclothing.com www.bargainclothing.com
A classic two-piece suit for under $60. A sparkly stretch-velvet evening dress for $39 (in sizes six through 16!). Need we say more? Browse the women's store, the boutique (with younger, cooler fashions), or the plus-size section at bargainclothing.com for great deals on clothes that won't go out of style. The site makes it easy to send a gift (complete with a card) right from the checkout page; they'll even send you an e-mail confirming that the gift was sent.

Bisou-Bisou www.bisou-bisou.com
Enchanting and slightly ethereal is how you'll find both the site and the clothes at Bisou-Bisou, designer Michele Bohbot's adventure in stretch and silk. The dresses, tops, skirts, and shoes here are hip, gorgeous, and very small—anyone above size four should consult the sizing chart, which recommends buying a size larger than you are. If you're unsure, use the store locator to find a Bisou-Bisou store and try before you buy.

ShoppingTheWorld www.shoppingtheworld.com (d)
Fashionistas will swoon over ShoppingTheWorld, an inspired e-store that aims to bring stylish duds from New York, Los Angeles, and London to your doorstep. The site is organized by neighborhood, so you can browse SoHo for trendy T-shirts, Fifth Avenue for Hermes scarves, or Melrose for punky baby clothes. There are also loads of articles on current trends, tips on what to do in each city, and a personal shopper who will hold everything in a "dressing room" while you shop.

Land's End www.landsend.com (c) (s)
Everyone's favorite catalog has gone from paper to pixel with class. Men, women, and kids will find sturdy styles for school, hiking, vacations, and casual workdays, all backed by reasonable prices and outstanding service. But what really stands out here are spectacular services like the personal virtual model, which allows women to view clothes on a virtual model of their body type, and the shop-with-a-friend feature, which lets you chat and browse the site with a friend halfway around the world. Amazing!

Club Monaco www.clubmonaco.com (d)
Young, well-cut clothes in solid colors are Club Monaco's hallmark, with tailored pants, tops, and jackets that easily make the transition from work to after-hours. Their user-friendly site lets you zoom in on fabrics (so you can really see that knit up close), and offers sample combinations in case you're stumped for an outfit. Club Monaco also has a makeup line with shades that compliment the clothes.

Kenneth Cole www.kennethcole.com
Silly product names aside, Kenneth Cole's sportswear, outerwear, shoes, and accessories can't be out-sleeked. Try the square toe boots (called Al Gor-ithms), a leather backpack (Knap-kin), or a black mini-trench (Joan of Dark) for a dose of New York cool. Are they expensive? You bet! But just one look at the quality and style here lets you know you're getting your money's worth.

Anthropologie www.anthropologie.com (s)
Boho cool meets urban chic at Anthropologie, a store whose buyers troll flea markets and estate sales from England to India to bring you funky clothing and housewares. Pick up an embroidered sari curtain, a velvet wrap skirt, or a country French wooden table; the prices run high, so be sure to browse the extensive sale links. The exceptionally courteous customer service policy assures that if you don't like your purchase, they will take care of you.

Orvis Online www.orvis.com
Because Orvis began by selling fly fishing supplies (back in 1856), it's no surprise that the company's focus remains on outdoorsy clothing. Not only can you purchase fly fishing and hunting supplies, men's and women's clothing, and travel and home accessories here, you can also learn how to shoot or fish at Orvis' special schools, or read a fly fishing how-to guide. Don't be deceived by the sports focus here, though; the clothes are stylish enough for any occasion.

NYstyle www.nystyle.com
If your wardrobe colors range from charcoal to black, NYstyle is your site. Actually, there are a few colorful items interspersed among the racks and racks of little black dresses here—in addition to men's and women's wear, you can buy gifts, handbags, cosmetics, stationery, and jewelry. The prices are steep, the merch is chic, and there are a few bargains to be had here and there. Search by category, price, best-sellers, and, of course, labels.

J. Jill www.jjill.com
Can you spell c-o-m-f-o-r-t? This "simple pleasures" headquarters offers a wide selection of work and casual clothes that you can live in—it almost makes the prospect of getting dressed before sunrise somewhat appealing. Search by category or head straight for the price-friendly links: Best Value and Now on Sale. Such beautiful words.

ESPRIT www.esprit.com

Head to ESPRIT for boutique-quality clothing at mall prices. The company's complete line of fashion-forward apparel is available on this site, with clear pictures that give a good sense of how the garments really look. You also get color, sizing, and accessory charts, and Web deals that make online shopping even better than a trip to a real dressing room.

Fashionmall.com www.fashionmall.com

Shopping variety without the typical mall mayhem. Fashionmall.com is a massive clothing and accessory resource with something for every taste and price range. Choose the Madison "floor" for finer threads, SoHo for cutting edge clothes, Galleria for brand names, or Main Street for basics. You'll also find fashion advice and trends for every season. Before you buy, be sure to read the return policies for the individual sites Fashionmall.com has patched you through to.

gap.com www.gap.com

Used to be there was a Gap on nearly every block—now there's one in every home! Point your browser to gap.com for jackets, slacks, cotton shirts, and classic jeans (15 styles), or treat yourself to sleepwear and seasonal specialty items. Should you decide your Gap purchase leaves something to be desired, just mail it back or return it to a store near you.

A-Wear www.awear.com

A-Wear donates a quarter from every item sold to non-profit groups in its home country (Canada) and globally—but don't think conscientiousness makes for square clothes. The men's, women's, and kids' apparel here has miles of style. Don't leave before you check out the A-wear-ness links, selected sites on art, news, and global issues.

Eddie Bauer www.eddiebauer.com

A torrential rainstorm and some soggy wool underwear were the inspiration that spurred Mr. Bauer to create his line of durable and weather-proof clothing. Since then, the company's stock has expanded to include camping accessories and home furnishings as well as men's and women's apparel—all available online. Don't miss the virtual dressing room at this site, where you can pair items together to see how they look before buying.

Hippies www.hippies.com

Don't let the name fool you—there's nothing crunchy about this shimmery hosiery store. Tights, hose, knee-highs, and body stockings are all available in a range of colors, sizes, and styles that will serve almost any lady with legs to show. The lack of a search function means that some browsing is necessary, but the simple, elegant site design eases the process.

Ujena.com www.ujena.com

A swimsuit site for the Muscle Beach crowd, Ujena.com has a full range of figure-flaunting (and sometimes fanny-flossing) bikinis and one-pieces. Unique picks include a leather swimsuit and a gauze bikini that turns transparent when wet. No worries, though—there are more traditional options. The sizing chart should help you find a good fit, and lets you order different sizes for the bikini top and bottom.

Caché www.cache.com
Laura Ashley would have a coronary surfing around Caché, but anyone in the market for 1,000-watt glamour will love these clothes. Feathered mini dresses, velvet illusion tops, and sequined evening wraps are among the choices available here . . . Hold on to your credit cards!

DesignerOutlet.com www.designeroutlet.com
Feed your Prada obsession or find a sizzling dress for tonight's dinner party. DesignerOutlet.com carries clothes from DKNY, Mizrahi, and other designers that only a fashion maven would know about. For inspiration, check the features page to see what hemline mayhem Cynthia Rowley is wreaking this season. The selection is weak for certain designers, but with clothes 50% off, you can buy twice as much!

Coldwater Creek www.coldwatercreek.com (S)
Come on in, the clothes are fine. Coldwater Creek sells traditional and conservative women's clothing, accessories, and home furnishings—think L.L. Bean with a slightly more "country casual" feel. The size selection is limited for some items (certain shoes, for example, were available only in sizes 6.5 and 7.5), but outstanding for others (dresses in small to 3X). The Instant Help customer service feature lets you type in a question for one of their reps, but given how long we waited for a response, you might be better off using the 24-hour toll-free number.

Fitigues www.fitigues.com
What's black, white, and comfortable all over? Fitigues, which combine hip styling and livable fabrics. Examples include a thermal party dress, a stretch-velvet cardigan, silk-cotton chinos, and a gray flannel vest. The selection is better for women than men, and includes a great maternity section. 14 days for returns.

eOFFprice www.eoffprice.com
With brands like Calvin Klein, Tommy Hilfiger, and Ralph Lauren and numbers like 30 to 70% off the retail price, this site is a must-surf for bargain hunters. The selection is variable, but for men's, women's, and children's clothing and accessories this cheap, it's worth checking back often.

RealSize.com www.realsize.com (C)
A community site and shopping destination for plus-sized women, RealSize.com offers a sampling of clothes from the Delta Burke and the Onyx Nite collections. Once you're through stocking up on stylish dresses, shirts, pants and jackets, be sure to visit RealHealth, which features health and nutrition advice, and RealEntertainment, a link to news stories and profiles of successful women.

JustMySize.com www.justmysize.com (S)
Plus-size women who are frustrated with lilliputian tops and one-size-fits-no-one pants will love JustMySize.com. The site offers fashions for work, workouts, and weekends, in a range of sizes that doesn't sacrifice flair for fit. You'll also find the foundations and pantyhose to complete your outfit, as well as Web bargains to save you a few bucks. Refunds are given even if you've worn the garment once.

Mark Shale www.markshale.com
Dress professionally and your business savvy soars. Mark Shale carries an elegant line of professional and casual clothes for both men and women. You can e-mail the experts with fashion questions, browse the selection of suits, sweaters, and jackets, or read Mark Shale's predictions for this season's fashion trends. Plus, customer help is plentiful and giftwrap is free.

LegwearDirect.com www.legweardirect.com
Tights, socks, and hosiery at significant discounts, direct from the manufacturer—who cares if it's LegwearDirect.com's own label? An average pair of tights here will run you around $5; even with the $3 shipping charge, they're still cheaper than designer label hose. The sizing information is buried in the frequently asked questions page, just in case you were wondering.

onehanesplace.com www.onehanesplace.com
With well-known names like Hanes, L'eggs, Playtex, and Wonderbra, onehanesplace.com could keep you in underwear up to your ears for years. Shop for bras, buy workout clothing or a pair of socks, or look to the closeout section for discounts and "slightly imperfect" merchandise. There's a men's store and a kid's store here, too.

VictoriasSecret.com www.victoriassecret.com

What is Victoria's secret? Perhaps it's the fact that her catalog's readership is predominantly male. Ladies, however, will find the Web site a convenient way to get the slinky bras and silky nighties the company is famous for. Additional Web features include a Bra Search (which helps overwhelmed shoppers select the level of push-up, padding, and wires they want) and the stunning selections in the Glamour Lounge.

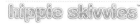

Hippie Skivvies www.hippieskivvies.com
Spice up your day with tie-dyed unmentionables from this quirky site—no one will ever guess you've got Hippie Skivvies on underneath that boring business suit! The underwear on offer here is comfortable, casual, and vaguely psychedelic. Choose boxers, thongs, or camisoles in a rainbow of crazy colors, and be sure to check out the "Skivvies Around the World" link, which has photos of folks posing in their skivvies at locations like Las Vegas and the leaning tower of Pisa.

The Bugle Boy Virtual Store www.bugleboy.com
Pardon me. Is that Bugle Boy you're surfing? For tough, well-made clothing to get down and dirty in, nothing beats Bugle Boy. You'll find outdoorsy styles for men, women, and boys at their e-store, which also provides a virtual playground that's amusing to visit even if it won't help you break in your new carpenter pants.

Men's Clothing

Thomas Pink www.thomaspink.com (s)
Real men wear pink–Thomas Pink, that is. This famed British store has a stunning array of men's shirts in the finest fabrics, as well as the cufflinks, sweaters, and silk ties to accompany them. While it's sometimes hard to find a specific item, great product descriptions and photos will help you along. Superb customer service includes a sizing and shrinkage guide, info on how to take care of your shirts, inexpensive alterations, free giftwrap, and 30 days for returns.

Paul Fredrick MenStyle Online www.paulfredrick.com
If your taste runs closer to conservative than casual, you'll love the superior variety of fabrics and styles available at Paul Frederick MenStyle. Customer service is limited to e-mail, and the pages are slow to load, but for clothing that's a cut above the rest, it's worth the minor hassle.

King Size Tall & Big www.kingsizemen.com (s)
"Size matters" is simply a shopping motto when you're a big or tall man. King Size Tall & Big has the extra large suits, casuals, shoes, jackets, pajamas, and sportswear you may have had trouble finding elsewhere. It's also got oft-neglected essentials like underwear, belts, and an extra large fanny pack. Customer service is available 24 hours a day, seven days a week at a toll-free number.

Ermenegildo Zegna www.ezegna.com
Go from dull to devastating in two quick steps: first, shed the Gap khakis; second, hightail it to Ermenegildo Zegna. The self-proclaimed leader in elegant menswear will have you looking dapper from cuff to collar in a matter of minutes. For casuals, browse Zegna Sport, the low key, high-style companion site. Clothes this slick do come at a price, though (try $725 for a cotton jacket).

Bachrach www.bachrach.com (s)
Fraying blazers and clip-on ties do not a snappy dresser make. Bachrach carries great-looking clothes for when you want to look put together–jewel-tone ties, Merino wool mock turtlenecks, and flannel trousers are among the offerings here. Considering the quality, you'll find the reasonable prices a pleasant surprise. Web shopping perks include free shipping, a store locator, express catalog ordering, and a Great Outfits page that can help you dress for that all-important first date.

Brooks Brothers www.brooksbrothers.com (d) (s)

Sporting the same sleek lines and sophisticated aura we've come to expect from the clothes, the Brooks Brothers Web site doesn't disappoint. The full line of corporate formal and country-club casual clothes is gathered together here in an easily-navigable interface. Satisfaction is guaranteed–should you change your mind after your sweater set arrives, just mail it back to their New Jersey headquarters for an exchange or credit.

Guyshop www.guyshop.com (d)
It takes one fine man to outshine clothes as cool as these. If you think you're up to the challenge, browse Guyshop's bundle of boutiques for stretch wool pants, Mental wristbands, and the basic black T in hipper-than-thou mesh. The graphics are superb, the prices are fair, and the clothes will have you itching for Saturday night. Buyer beware: your Guyshop garb just might go to your head.

International Male www.internationalmale.com (c)
Faster than a speeding bullet, International Male can turn your boring clothes into an outfit with panache. The IM Essentials section dresses the Clark Kent in you, with weekday basics like a cashmere mock turtleneck, pleated pants, and a suede blazer. Go to On the Edge for outfits to bring out your inner Superman: leather pants, a sparkly vest, and a leopard-print thong. The clothes run a bit flashy (a silk pirate shirt is considered essential) but you can guarantee that all eyes will be on you.

Ties.Com www.ties.com
A great little specialty e-store. Browse Ties.Com by color, by designer, or by pattern, price range, and even category (animals, architecture, etc.). Whether your taste runs toward the sublime (a $96 black and silver Italian silk tie) or the artless (a $16 Stone Cold Steve Austin "Whoop-Ass 101" pattern), they've got you covered. Neckwear novices should click on What Knot to Do, which should help you master the basics sans strangulation.

2(x)ist www.2xist.com
For a visual lesson in contour pouch vs. fly-front that's as artfully done as it is illustrative, 2(x)ist is the site to visit. The five styles of briefs, two kinds of boxers, and three undershirts available here are shown front and back in attractive black and white pictures. All are white cotton and range in size from 28 to 40. Basic white underwear never had it so good.

WebUndies.com www.webundies.com
For guys who never outgrew their Batman Underoos, WebUndies.com sells briefs and boxers with such snazzy designs as Star Wars, Scooby-Doo, Curious George and WCW Wrestling. You'll either be the pride of the locker room or the target for ridicule, depending on your gym.

Kids & Teens

MXGonline www.mxgonline.com
Breaking trends for the under-20 set. MXGonline doesn't simply cover the trend of the season or the week—log on here to find out what's hot *today*. That's right: the site is so fashion-forward you might start to feel old just surfing. Browse the clothes, go to "Celeb Central" to bask in celebrity coolness, and be sure to check back often—what's in today may be out tomorrow.

Healthtex www.healthtex.com ⓒ ⓓ
Welcome to Playville Hill! This ultra-cute site is set up so that kids can have fun picking out their own clothes. The shop has clothing for infants to 12-year-olds, though it's aimed at the younger set. Clothes for both girls and boys are well-crafted and designed for heavy use, so girls don't get stuck in frilly dresses while the boys are out having fun in the tree-house. Parents can click on the Neighborly Advice section for home safety tips, the Doctor's Office for vaccination information, and the Links booth for site recommendations.

BellaKids www.bellakids.com
Everything *bella* for children—clothes, shoes, toys, bedding, and furniture. BellaKids selects high-quality items from well-known children's designers like Blue Moon and Sylvia White. This is special occasion clothing, beautiful and well made, suited for dress-up and parties more than the playground. Enjoy the pictures—the clothes will probably never look that clean and unwrinkled again.

Oliebollen.com www.oliebollen.com
Oliebollen.com believes in living childishly. Fun, bright, and sturdily-designed, the apparel (and the site) is designed for kids who love playful clothes like rubber boots with frog faces or jeans with embroidered butterflies. Search by brand, category, and age range, or open the mysterious Door No. 3 to unlock the deal of the day. There's also a short animated video here put together especially for Oliebollen.com shoppers.

OshKosh B'Gosh
www.oshkoshbgosh.com
The funniest name and the coolest overalls are at OshKosh B'Gosh. Shop here for denim basics for babies and kids, as well as stylish accessories like a little denim car seat headrest. Expectant moms will have to shop elsewhere for maternity overalls (no women's clothes here), but the large selection and frequent sales make this site worth a stop.

Hanna Andersson www.hannaandersson.com
Hanna Andersson makes clothes that your grandmother could have worn when she was a kid—high-quality cotton and corduroy basics that with-stand serious dirt and time in the washing machine. Apparel for babies, toddlers, boys, and girls is available here in a great range of sizes and colors; there is also some women's and unisex clothing. The friendly return policy welcomes returns and exchanges by mail, and an e-mail feedback page lets you ask any question you didn't find answered in the FAQ.

Gymboree
www.gymboree.com
Bright colors, quality fabrics, and a useful sizing chart (by weight and height, as well as age) make this a welcome site for parents too busy to hit the mall. Scroll down to buy clothes as separates, or take advantage of coordinated sets when you don't have time to mix and match. Cute packaging and gift certificates, too.

gapkids.com www.gapkids.com (s)
Where do Gap grown-ups come from? From Gap Kids, of course. The online version of the store is easy enough for a child to navigate but, luckily for parents, requires a grown-up's credit card for purchase. Find all the elementary school fashion basics, from backpacks and hats to small-sized versions of the Gap's classic khakis and vests.

dELiAs.cOm www.delias.com (d) (s)
Shop dELiAs.cOm and you'll be the best-dressed teenager around, guaranteed. They've got everything from retro glasses frames ($8) to elegant wool sweaters ($36) that are destined to make you the envy of your algebra class. When you're done shopping, visit dELiAs.cOm's sister site, the Web 'zine gURL.com, for loads of teen-centered articles and advice. It's just like shopping with your friends!

dot dot dash www.dotdotdash.com (d) (s)
From that super-saccharine yet ever-appealing dELiA's comes dot dot dash, a site geared toward girls sizes seven to 16. The clothes are simple and trendy, and designed to fit within the average girl's clothing allowance. Surf here for games, screen savers, and lots of cotton-poly blend. Shipping is free for orders over 40 dollars.

Alloy.com www.alloy.com (c) (d) (s)
Alloy.com is advice, entertainment, music, games, gossip, and, oh yeah, shopping. Teens should check out the fab boutiques here offering clothes, accessories, bathing gear, music, and fun products for your room (like an inflatable palm tree and a leopard-print computer cover). The stuff here really is cool, even if you do have put up with liberal usage of the words "awesome" and "rad."

droog www.droog.com (d)
Droog isn't a site for mincing words (click Consume to shop), but when you're the bomb.com, you needn't be bashful. Aimed at teenage boys, the site offers high school fashion at its coolest, with pictures and sizing info that make it easy to buy online. The items are affordably priced to fit within the budget of the average after-school McJob, but if you're really strapped, skip the shopping and link to the Scam Free Gifts section, which shows you where you can trade survey answers for free stuff all over the Net.

Accessories

Dooney & Bourke www.dooney.com (d)

Look to Dooney & Bourke for gorgeous leather bags and accessories that last a lifetime. The site's simple and elegant design (with large pictures) makes it easy to shop for handbags, backpacks, wallets, even a chic leather Palm Pilot case. But Dooney quality will cost you—around $150 for a wallet, $300 for a bag.

VillageHatShop.com www.villagehatshop.com (c)

Cap, chapeau, headdress, or hat: if you can put it on your head, VillageHatShop.com probably sells it. Nearly all are affordable (read: less than $80), stylish, and easy to fit using the site's hat size guide. While you're at it, browse the comprehensive glossary of hat-related terms or read fun hat facts. (Did you know that hatters actually went mad from inhaling mercury fumes while making felt hats?)

eBags www.ebags.com (s)

Ditch the pack mule look and get from point A to point B in style. EBags has a garment bag for your clothes, a messenger bag for your books, and a golf carrier for your clubs. For the packing-impaired, the bag recommendations and Ask the Road Warrior pages are filled with helpful advice. Free UPS shipping and frequent-flyer miles for registered shoppers.

Fossil www.fossil.com (d)

Nothing endures like a Fossil—a classic line of watches that won't melt your credit card. Now you can see the full line of Fossil products online, including handbags, wallets, and key fobs, in addition to watches. Cool limited-edition timepieces are also available for your favorite Pink Panther or Beatles fan.

netsetgoods.com www.netsetgoods.com

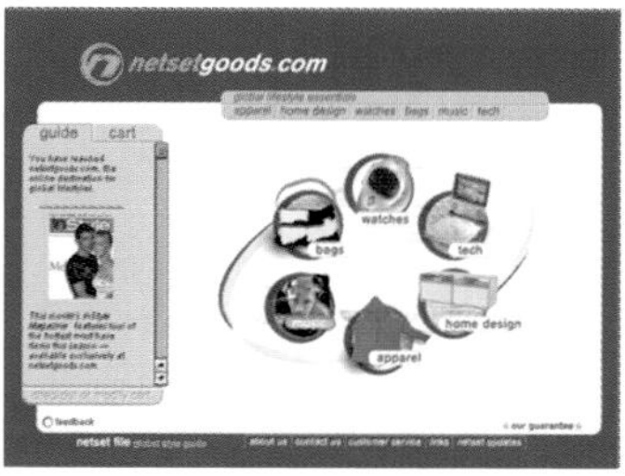

You may not be a member of the jet set, but you can be part of the Net set. Score cutting-edge stuff from the cities that do it best, namely Los Angeles, London, Tokyo, New York, and Paris. The hippest handbags, tube tops, and watches are collected here, along with a hand-picked selection of electronic music and super cases for toting your new CDs. You may not get the frequent-flyer miles, but you're sure to get the style points.

Ashford.com www.ashford.com (c) (s)

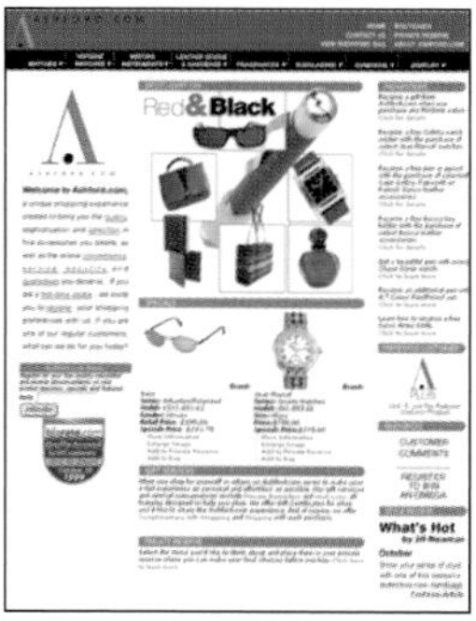

Exclusive and elegant watches, pens, silk scarves, and jewelry for discriminating tastes. Ashford.com's accessories are gorgeous and carefully selected. And with equally superlative customer service (free shipping, free gift-wrapping, and 60 days for returns), you might just get used to the high life.

WatchZone www.watchzone.com Ⓒ Ⓢ

This site's combination of brand names (20 total, including Swatch, Timex, G-Shock, and Calvin Klein) and supercheap Hot Deals should make it the first stop on any watch shopping trip. Plus, if you find the same watch for less somewhere else, WatchZone will match the competitor's price. Free FedEx shipping on all orders.

Wristwatch.com www.wristwatch.com

For quality wristwear in a New York minute, visit Wristwatch.com. The vast assortment available here includes activity-specific watches (running, yachting, wind surfing), as well as ones with special features like a thermometer, a moon phase tracker, or a perpetual calendar. If your current timepiece is giving you trouble, access the bank of instruction manuals to root out the problem. Scanning the long pages can be a bit tedious, but the selection makes it worthwhile.

Sunglasses 2000 www.sunglasses2000.com

Don't hide your pretty peepers behind last year's lame frames. Point your browser to Sunglasses 2000 and choose from designers like Giorgio Armani, Gucci, Ralph Lauren, and Versace. Or, for bargain eyewear, check the Monthly Special page, which offers items at 10 to 15% off. The product descriptions are wanting, but you can always e-mail customer service in English, Italian, or Spanish *para más información*.

The Sunglass City www.thesunglasscity.com

Web years are a lot like dog years: one year counts as several. The Sunglass City has been the online source for sunglasses since 1987—making it ancient by Web standards—and for good reason. The site has all the famous names like Oakley, Vuarnet, and Black Flys, at big, big discounts. You may need to phone in to get pricing information on some selections, but for Ray Bans at half off, you owe it to your retinas to make the call.

OpticalSite www.opticalsite.com

Eyewear savings that must be seen to be believed. OpticalSite sells contacts, frames, and lenses at discount prices; if you find the same pair elsewhere for less, they'll refund you 110%. Try the site's Contact Lens selector to find the lenses you need, or read the interesting, if small, features section for the latest eyewear news and reviews. Express shipping is only $8.50 (2-day service), but customer service feedback is limited to e-mail.

Yak Pak www.yakpak.com Ⓢ

A bike messenger's dream, Yak Pak offers a wide selection of trendy bags designed to hold lots of cargo without being unwieldy. Styles include Vexed, Holster, DJ, and Messenger, and all come with a lifetime guarantee that makes the semi-steep prices seem more down-to-earth. Plus, with a clearly posted privacy policy, friendly customer service folk, and a return policy that includes exchanges for different colors, this site lets you know you can shop without hesitation.

Coach www.coach.com (S)

The soft leather and distinctive stitching of a baseball glove were the inspiration that led to the Coach company. Now, more than half a century later, you can buy its renowned handbags, watches, and travel gear online. Treat yourself to a monogrammed satchel, or use the Corporate Gifts section to find a classy business gift. The prices are a study in inflation, but keep in mind that you're paying for a little history, a lot of quality, and impeccable customer service.

Samsonite®

Samsonite www.samsonite.com

Shop Samsonite for tough suitcases, casual bags, and business accessories that won't cave at the baggage claim. Big, clear product descriptions make it easy to choose a bag, even if the site's design leaves something to be desired. And the warranties will leave you certain that your BVDs will get to DFW A-OK.

PashminaTrunkshow.Com www.pashminatrunkshow.com

Wearing pashmina is a test in turn-of-the-century fashion etiquette. First, you have to know what pashmina is. Then you have to master the art of appropriately wrapping, draping, or slinging it about yourself. Never fear—PashminaTrunkShow.Com will walk you through your purchase with style guides, color charts, and perspectives on the big decision: wrap or shawl?

PilgrimDesigns.com www.pilgrimdesigns.com

Leave the matching purse and pumps to Donna Reed—for handbags with flair, your first stop should be PilgrimDesigns.com. The selection is inspired by "interesting travels, beautiful cultures, a favorite novel, and much more." Treat your inner femme fatale to a glittery, flashy clutch, or go exotic with the Asian-tinged Orient Express line. If you're set on color coordination, give it a modern edge by choosing a lip, eye, and cheek color to go with your new bag.

Computers

CNET.com www.cnet.com (C)

Well organized, jam-packed with information, and absolutely indispensable. If you're in the market for hardware or software, CNET.com takes the guesswork out of tech-buying with excellent product reviews, price comparisons, and buying guides. After finding out exactly what a Dell Dimension XPS T5 MiniTower will and will not do, you'll know whether to bid on it at the Tech Auction page or move on to another machine.

egghead.com + Onsale www.onsale.com

Forget the day after Thanksgiving; the sale is going on all year at egghead.com + Onsale. The newly merged e-tailers sell computers, software, and electronics for a song. Think you can do better? Name your price at the online auctions here. You just might walk away with Norton Antivirus at a sickeningly cheap price. Comparison shopping within the site isn't very easy, but with prices 5 to 10% cheaper than other online megastores, you may not need to comparison shop.

Gateway www.gateway.com

There's a reason why Gateway's black-and-white spotted boxes have become such a familiar sight: their computers are powerful and user friendly. Shop at Gateway for desktops, portables, and networking devices. Their tech-support pages are some of the best around, giving easy-to-follow instructions on how to construct the perfect machine for your needs. Easy, no-hassle shopping.

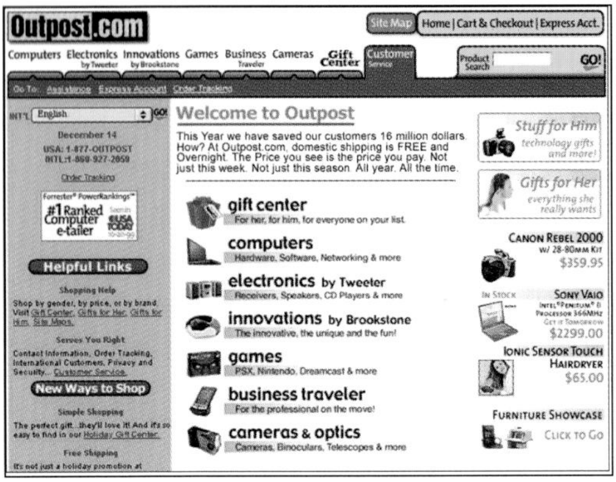

Outpost.com
www.outpost.com Ⓢ

Whether you want a huge monitor to double as a movie screen or a dinky hand-held computer, Outpost.com will ship it to you overnight for free. With that in mind, go ahead and pile your shopping cart high with desktop computers, patio furniture, and stereo speakers—there are 140,000 products to choose from. The site doesn't have side-by-side product comparisons and reviews; come to Outpost.com when you know what you want and you want a deal.

Insight www.insight.com Ⓒ

Routers, surge protectors, switchboxes, video cards, hand-helds ... if it's computer-related, you'll find it at Insight, which has better-than-average prices on thousands of brand-name products. Quick-install guides, online software classes, and performance tips round out the offerings here. Live support is at a minimum, though; this spot favors rugged individualists who can figure things out in their own time and on their own dime.

MacMall
www.macmall.com

MacMall

Mac devotees rejoice: MacMall offers "insanely great deals" on software, hardware, and iMacs in all their many flavors. The site also has a Memory Configurator service that will tell you exactly what you need to upgrade your system, a list of current hot discounts, and free shipping on orders of $500 or more. How do ya like them apples?

MicroWarehouse www.microwarehouse.com

With nice big pictures of all the items on offer here, the MicroWarehouse site looks exactly like the catalog—right down to that picture of the blond customer service rep. (Who is she?) You must register to buy here, but doing so will get you straightforward deals on PCs, Macs, handhelds, supplies, and more. The product descriptions are detailed and clear; scroll down to the bottom to see other products that MicroWarehouse recommends to go with your purchase.

eCOST.com

eCOST.com www.ecost.com
Offering instant rebates or free ground shipping on most purchases, eCOST.com can knock a significant amount off of what you'd normally spend on a high-ticket item like an HP LaserJet printer or Iomega PC Card. In-depth product information and a team of computer specialists lend peace of mind while you're shopping in unfamiliar territory (i.e., The Land of the Flatbed Scanners). You can also shop here for electronics. The one drawback? No customer service after 6 p.m. PST.

CDW.com www.cdw.com
If you're about to set up a business or are planning to upgrade your equipment, head for CDW.com, which can sell or lease you a broad range of hardware, software, and networking equipment. You may find better prices elsewhere, but the hands-on customer service team can save you valuable time and money by solving incompatibilities. The list of manufacturer rebates and coupons can also lower your bottom line considerably.

cozone.com www.cozone.com ⓒ
Cozone.com used to be CompUSA, but you would never know it by looking: the new site is totally independent from its parent company, with different prices and different products. We're all for the change: cozone.com's emphasis on information makes it a whole lot easier to decide on hardware, software, and electronics. Click on the notebook section, for example, and a yellow shaded box offers advice from ZDNet comparing prices and performance for various models. Great concept.

NECX www.necx.com
Sporting a refreshingly simple design, NECX is a business-to-business dealer whose site is geared toward consumers. With side-by-side product comparisons and the incredibly useful list of manufacturer rebates and coupons, customers can get sizable bargains on the semiconductors, electronic components, computer products, and networking equipment they need to stay competitive. The one thing that NECX doesn't offer is free telephone ordering; if you don't want to buy online, you'll have to pay $25 for the phone call.

HardwareStreet.com www.hardwarestreet.com ⓓ
Printers and desktops and keyboards, oh my! If you're in the market for hardware, no matter how obscure, there's a good chance you'll find a bargain here. The simple, well-designed front page makes it supereasy to locate what you seek, be it memory, processors, printers, or computer systems.

HardwareStreet.com

The Memory Broker www.compbroker.com
If your Mac or PC moves slower than Florida motorists, head for the Memory Broker, a decidedly unglitzy site that will sell you increased RAM or a brand new hard drive designed to get you zipping along the information highway in a flash. Not sure how to proceed? Click on the Information Bank, which tells you what will work with your machine.

HP Shopping Village www.shopping.hp.com Ⓒ
It takes an HP Shopping Village to get you this impressive an array of Hewlett Packard's computers, printers, digital cameras, scanners, and software. Select the item you're looking for and up pop pictures of your choices, with links to accessories you might need. So, while you're shopping for a camera, you can price printers, adapters, and memory cards as well. The Home Office tutorials are simple and easy to follow, and multilingual customer service reps can help you in Swedish, Spanish, or Simplified Chinese.

Zones.com www.zones.com
A computer shopping site that divides its 100,000 products into easily navigable zones: PC, Mac, and Business Solutions. There are some terrific buys here, thanks to weekly sales and special promotions, plus an Auction Zone, where you'll find everything from HP scanners to IBM monitors up for bid. Zones.com deserves kudos for providing a manageable shopping environment—and the cool Tech Zone section—but be sure to read the return policy carefully before you buy. Zones.com charges a 30% restocking fee on some hardware returns.

PC Mall www.pcmall.com Ⓢ
The self-proclaimed "mall with it all" makes up in its product line what it lacks in a food court. PC Mall's custom configuration service will help you pick and choose the equipment you need to get your home office up and running the next day, while exclusive deals and special offers can net you great deals on brand names like Apple, Epson, Microsoft, and Toshiba. Excellent customer service (including 24-hour phone access) lets you shop with confidence.

Buyonet www.buyonet.com
Offering software programs in 20 different languages, Buyonet has thousands of downloadable titles, everything from Lotus Organizer to IntelliGolf Birdie. All the programs are delivered electronically, thereby cutting out the packaging and shipping costs that can otherwise weigh down your bill. And speaking of bills, don't worry about changing those Italian *lire* for American greenbacks ... Buyonet accepts more than 20 types of currency. *Bene*!

PalmGear H.Q. www.palmgear.com
Fans of the famed pint-sized computer won't want to miss PalmGear H.Q. With hardware, software, accessories, and cleaning supplies, this Palm Pilot headquarters should be your first stop for everything from a carrying case to a new accounting program. While you're shopping, read the enormous FAQ page or the Tips and Tricks section to learn how to boost your Palm power. And don't miss the great downloads—the next boring board meeting will be much more bearable with a bingo game, a map of the Grand Canyon, or a wine guide discretely in hand.

Chumbo.com www.chumbo.com

A computer without software is like peanut butter without jelly, like TV sans remote, like Fred without Ginger: totally useless. Complete your machine with software from Chumbo.com; they've got Mac and PC programs that can do everything from designing Pokémon cards to transcribing your lecture notes. Chumbo.com's super-navigable (and cool-looking) design has garnered accolades from *PC Magazine* and *U.S. News & World Report*. Check it out to see why.

Jumbo www.jumbo.com

Step right up, folks, to the greatest site for shareware and freeware on the Net. Featuring more than 300,000 programs, Jumbo's got tons of fun stuff, including games, MP3s and cool screensavers. The software demos can be a bit frustrating, cutting you off just when a program gets useful or interesting, but that's probably the point. An endlessly fascinating place to surf, it's practically impossible to walk away empty-handed.

edu.com www.edu.com

edu.com students get it

Having Ramen for dinner again? Scrimping college students will find a friend in edu.com, a site with tech discounts especially for students. Save up to 70% on computer hardware, software, textbooks, and long distance. The site also has useful user guides on stuff like banking and credit card security so you can keep track of what little money you do have. Plus, get points for shopping, completing surveys, and referring friends to the site.

Iomega www.iomega.com

Zip, Jaz, Clik!—are they expletives or just Iomega products? This company's storage cartridges have all but eaten up floppy disks. Handy online ordering means you won't have to schlep to Staples during your lunch break; the prices here are slightly cheaper than in stores. Iomega's site also offers product support (The Zip ate my homework!), as well as information on lesser-known but similarly strange-sounding Iomega items like Buz and Ditto.

IBM www.ibm.com

At Big Blue's Web store, you won't find any computers designated by flavor. What you will find, however, is a hardcore selection of PC products for business, home, and travel. ThinkPads? Affirmative. Thin Clients? Yep. Software, servers, switches? Yes, yes, and yes. Cutting-edge types won't want to miss the free demos, beta patches, and fix-it advice available here. As for customer service, IBM gives you four ways (phone, fax, email, postal mail) to connect with a representative.

Beyond.com www.beyond.com

Software, software, and more software. Beyond.com has more than 50,000 titles for sale and 1.6 million that can be immediately downloaded from the site. Check out the cool Top 10 List or use the site's recommendation guide to find a gift. Terrific design; easy to navigate.

Compaq www.compaq.com
What good is the info superhighway when you're still driving an Edsel? Compaq has computing solutions for home, office, and small business that will get you zooming along in no time. Can't afford one off the showroom floor? Access the Factory Outlet, which features refurbished machines for less. An extensive menu of services is also available online (like free training for small businesses).

The Apple Store store.apple.com
Whether you've got a hankering for blueberry, lime, grape, or tangerine, the world's most colorful computer store can set you up with a model that's guaranteed to make your mouth water. Never fear, you won't be stymied by tech talk here; product descriptions are simple, informative, and comprehensible. Looks like the competition still has some lessons to learn from Apple.

Dell.com www.dell.com
Dell's site may not give you a warm and fuzzy feeling, but it can help you install, manage, and upgrade your computer in two shakes of a lamb's tail. Sure, you can probably find better prices at the bigger discount stores, but they won't be able to customize your system the way these folks can. Best of all, Dell.com is prepared to serve customers in more than 67 countries. Ah, the joys of doing business with the big guys!

Software BuyLine www.softwarebuyline.com
Whether you've been burned by the Melissa Virus or are bored senseless at work, check out Software BuyLine, which has a terrific selection of software to take care of all your business and personal needs. Programs cover a wide range of interests: try Kiplinger Tax Cut, Cosmopolitan Virtual Makeover, ResumeMaker Deluxe, Conflict Catcher, or Cyber Patrol. In short, everything you need to assist, educate, and entertain yourself.

Consumer Guides

Consumer Reports Online www.consumerreports.org ⓒ
For authoritative, unbiased evaluations of everything from hiking boots to laptops and national parks, a subscription to Consumer Reports Online might be the best $3.95 you spend this month. Members are also entitled to monthly newsletters on subjects like health and travel, and spotlights on particular products. Cheapskates need not despair: the site does have some free features, like lists of safety alerts and recalls.

ConsumerREVIEW.com www.consumerreview.com ⓒ
A simple and powerful idea: product reviews written by consumers. Read any one of 105,000 reviews in categories like sports and leisure, electronics, and baby gear, all written by people who actually bought the product. Or jump to one of ConsumerREVIEW.com's 15 sister sites for reviews and information on skiing, PC games, audio equipment, and cars, to name a few. There are even top product picks in various categories with quotes from—you guessed it—consumers.

Productopia www.productopia.com ⓒ

Sleek lines, chrome accents, a high-speed engine—you have to take a lot into consideration when shopping for a ... blender. Productopia is a gold mine of consumer advice and product information for large items (cars, computers) as well as smaller ones (eyebrow tweezers). Click on a category to see which brands get high marks for quality, style, and value, then read their bullet-point buying basics to jump start your shopping trip. The site also offers a complete menu of consumer reviews, discussions, and related links.

Deja.com www.deja.com ⓒ ⓓ

To discuss Prada bags with a rabid fan or digital cameras with others who bought them, dial up Deja.com. The site hosts discussion groups on just about any product you would ever want to buy (thousands of them) and rates the product according to user input. Though the user comments are only variously reliable, when taken together, they do provide valuable insight into a purchase. This is also a fun place to browse, find out what's new and cool, and peek in on the online community.

WebWatchdog www.webwatchdog.com

WebWatchdog relies on consumers to report on the best e-merchants on the Web, so the featured sites won't necessarily be the biggest or most famous. Still, it's worth browsing here for detailed merchant ratings, profiles, and policies. Each report is accompanied by helpful icons that indicate whether or not the site offers secure transactions, order tracking, or international shipping.

TRUSTe www.truste.org ⓒ

Want to protect your personal information online? Dial up TRUSTe, a nonprofit organization working to ensure the privacy of online shoppers. The site lets you look up merchants, review their privacy policies, and file complaints against errant stores. A word of caution, though: TRUSTe has come under fire for giving its seal to dubious organizations, so think twice before giving your information to any Web site, even one that is TRUSTe approved.

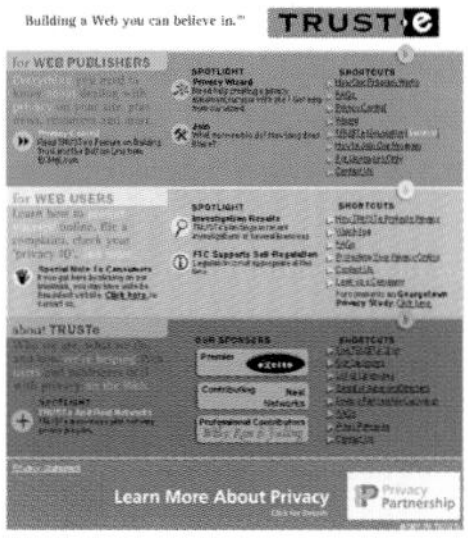

Epinions.com www.epinions.com ⓒ

Epinions.com compiles product reviews from average Joes who have a passion for a certain subject, be it cars, computers, electronics, travel, or movies. Read the biographies of reviewers to judge whose tastes most closely match your own, or link to the most popular contributors. The content is informative and endlessly surfable (in our epinion).

Gomez.com www.gomez.com ⓒ ⓓ

Gomez.com has taken those little comment cards you might find at your favorite restaurant and applied them to the online world. Of course they've given them a fancy name ("Internet Scorecards"), but the idea is the same. Sites are rated by consumers and ranked in categories such as ease of use, customer confidence, and overall cost. Although the lists are a bit superstore-heavy (lots of Amazon.coms and Borderses), the content is enlightening.

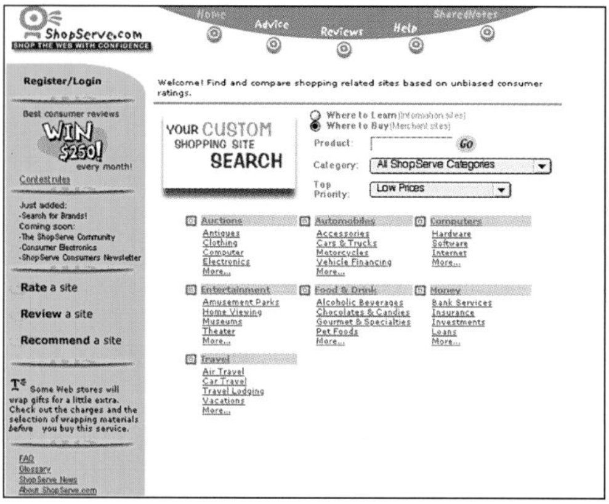

ShopServe.com www.shopserve.com

Don't waste time shopping at a site whose links load at the speed of mud. Check out ShopServe.com's reviews before you point your browser. See whether a site takes credit cards, check out their reliability rating, and take note of which sections are too cool to miss. Though the list of critiques is limited, what's here is promising.

BBBOnLine www.bbbonline.org

Separating the respectable from the disreputable. Before an online business can receive the Better Business Bureau's reliability seal, BBB representatives visit the company's physical location and verify its advertising claims. Browse their site for an alphabetical list of companies that participate in the online reliability program, or search for the name of the company you're thinking of patronizing. If you feel you've been ripped off, you can file a complaint and get assistance in resolving your dispute.

BizRate.com www.bizrate.com ⓒ

An extensive shopping guide with unbiased merchant ratings, BizRate.com is a reliable tool for finding safe e-stores. Click on a store to get a full report on delivery, returns, privacy policies, and secure ordering. Plus, BizRate.com will actually reward you (yes, that means money) for shopping online through their site. Just sign up for a BizRater e-mail address, use it every time you shop online, and BizRate.com will give you the commission that they get for referring your business. Neat idea.

Federal Trade Commission Consumer Protection
www.ftc.gov/ftc/consumer.htm

Though the design is unimaginative, the Consumer Protection section of the FTC's Web site will educate even the most naive Internet novice. The E-commerce and the Internet link leads you to dozens of documents (some in downloadable PDF format) on protecting your privacy. While you may have to wade through some bureaucratic jargon, on the whole the information here is clear, to-the-point, and relevant.

Department Stores & Superstores

Netmarket.com
www.netmarket.com
Blackbelt shoppers may love the thrill of the chase, but regular people just want to find great prices, fast. Enter Netmarket.com, a supersite for electronics, clothes, books, etc. that guarantees its members the lowest prices on its 800,000 products. Sure, you'll have to shell out a $70 annual membership fee, but if you find the product for less somewhere else, Netmarket.com will pay you the difference plus 35%. Guests have limited access to the deals here, so go ahead and browse before you join.

The Online Spiegel Catalog www.spiegel.com (s)
"Spiegel" means mirror in German, but in English, it's synonymous with dependable style. Now you can forgo the phonebook-sized catalog and get the same clothing, furniture, and electronics from Spiegel's sleek online store. Register a personalized wish list, check out the gift suggestions, or link to Spiegel's outlet division. Three different mailing options make returning unwanted items easy.

Value America www.valueamerica.com
Kind of like Sears, only bigger and online. With more than 20 departments, Value America has everything you want plus stuff you never even knew you needed (the food processing accessories alone will make your head spin). You can even get heavy-duty appliances like refrigerators and stoves here. Before checking out, be sure to read the return policy for your item; some merit a restocking fee, others aren't returnable at all.

Target.com www.target.com (d) (s)
Who ever said Target wasn't cool? The brand has had a makeover and it shows on their site, which sports a hip design and amazing product shots that rival the high-end department stores. Shop here for everything you usually shop here for: clothes, music, school supplies, housewares—you name it. The Web Price Cut links in each section spell out exactly which items have been discounted for Net shoppers.

macys.com www.macys.com
New York shoppers know it as the real miracle on 34th Street, but now everyone from Kansas to Canada can access Macy's online. Where else can you find Movado watches, Calvin Klein khakis, DKNY jeans, and Borghese exfoliant all in one place? You can also take advantage of the online Gift Express for your next birthday or baby shower, or purchase a gift certificate. You'll have a full sixty days to return items by mail or to drop them by a brick-and-mortar store should you enjoy battling the crowds.

Wal-Mart Online www.walmart.com ⓒ

Exactly what you'd expect from Wal-Mart Online. There are no frills or fancy graphics here, just tons of merchandise (60,000 items for sale) and some unusually helpful services–including realtors and a tire and lube locator service. Even online, it's hard to imagine where they'll put it all.

The JCPenney Internet Store www.jcpenney.com ⓢ

Mothers know it as a prime destination for back-to-school clothes, but JCPenney is more than just apparel. Shop here for an inexpensive vacuum, a pair of comfy slippers, or a bouclé sweater for under 20 bucks. Online shoppers can also access Web-exclusive services like a fashion advice column, toy safety recall listings, and a useful gift finder. Clear, complete instructions on returns are provided, whether you want to send the item back by mail or run it into a JCPenney store.

Sears.com www.sears.com ⓒ

Sears deserves praise for putting together a Web site that's sleek, understated, and easy to surf, which is just what you want from a store of this magnitude. Not only is there plenty of well-priced merchandise for your home, car, and yard (no clothing yet), there are also pages and pages of advice on doing all sorts of odd jobs. When worse comes to worst, hapless do-it-yourselfers can even call upon the repair specialists here.

Amazon.com www.amazon.com ⓢ

Remember when Amazon.com was just a cool online bookseller? Now the gargantuan e-tailer has added music, DVDs, electronics, toys, software, auctions, and zShops to its staggering product line. We still love classic features like "Customers who bought this book also bought ...", but there are some noteworthy innovations, like easy one-click shopping. Will Amazon.com lose its focus by trying to be everything to everyone? The jury's still out.

BUY.COM
The Internet Superstore

BUY.COM www.buy.com

No need to wonder what it's all about at BUY.COM and no surprises either. The super-site sells electronics, computers, music, and videos from brands like Epson, Hewlett-Packard, HP, and Sony. It's a solid, no frills site, obviously designed to make BUYing easy and hassle-free. There's also free shipping on sale items and a useful front-page link to FedEx and UPS tracking.

neimanmarcus.com www.neimanmarcus.com ⓓ

Zebra-striped hat boxes, alligator billfolds, monogrammed bath towels, vermeil chess sets ... for gifts with distinction, shop at neimanmarcus.com. Is it expensive? Yes. Fun to shop? You bet your life! The beautiful photographs, charming product descriptions, and great design indicate that these folks know how to combine commerce with style. Returns can be mailed back or taken into a store for merchandise credit.

Bloomingdale's
www.bloomingdales.com

Go ahead—fill your big brown bag to the brim at Bloomingdale's online. The store that started as a hoop skirt shop now has designer clothes, jewelry, and housewares. The customer service page is brusque but to the point, listing a toll-free number and directing you to check your invoice for return information. Just remember—it's all fun and games until the credit card statement arrives in the mail.

Nordstrom www.nordstrom.com ⓒ ⓢ

Some would say you haven't lived until you've huddled outside Nordstrom at daybreak, waiting (with a herd of other people) for the Half Yearly Sale to start. We, however, prefer the far more pleasant experience of shopping at the store's swank Web site. The same products are offered here, and finding sale items requires no pushing or shoving. Nordstrom's notoriously courteous customer service is in evidence here, too; to return an item, either head to a local store or stick it in the postage-paid envelop they include. They will, however, subtract the $3.95 charge from your refund, unless you paid with your Nordstrom card.

Costco Online www.costco.com ⓢ

Costco Online's wholesale pricing and mammoth stock give new meaning to the term "power shopping." While the site doesn't offer the bulk food that made Costco famous, online shoppers can still get a huge range of family-sized stuff (70 ounces of shampoo!), as well as electronics, home wares, and sporting goods on the cheap. Returns can be taken to any of the 300 Costco warehouses, open seven days a week (though you'd be wise to avoid Saturday). And if you ever doubt the worth of the membership price, they'll refund it in full.

Kmart www.kmart.com

Forget the flashing blue lights, the Rosie O'Donnell cameos, the "attention Kmart shoppers." The best way to take advantage of Kmart's low, low prices is online, with new department pages being added daily. A word of advice: figure out what you want before you go sifting through the content—weak product descriptions and a difficult-to-navigate design may trip up casual browsing. The customer service section seems to be more about how customers can serve Kmart rather than vice versa.

Debenhams www.debenhams.co.uk

Everything to woo that special someone. British department store Debenhams carries gifts, flowers, and housewares that are traditional in idea but current in execution. Pick up a silver necklace with a modern, square pendant, a metallic radio made of stackable cubes, or a bouquet of white lilies—perfect for birthdays, brides-to-be, or just because. Different return policies and guarantees apply to each of the three categories, so read up before you pay up.

Service Merchandise www.servicemerchandise.com
Service Merchandise calls itself "America's leading jeweler," but that's somewhat misleading. This mega-site sells not only jewelry (diamonds, silver, pearls, gold), but also electronics, sporting goods, luggage, furniture, toys, and more, all of it at a rather impressive discount (up to 50% off on some items). Whether you want an Italian foosball table or a treadmill, you'd be hard-pressed to find it cheaper elsewhere.

iQVC www.iqvc.com
Home-shopping aficionados will recognize the name as "Quality, Value, Convenience"—to everyone else, it's the first name in call-in shopping. The folks at QVC have managed to bring their trademark pluck to the Web, pitching the same vast array of items in electronics, home furnishings, beauty, collectibles, toys, and jewelry. The "Last Minute Clicks" section encourages impulse buying as only QVC can.

RedTag.com www.redtag.com
Folks who make a regular practice of clipping coupons and scouring newspaper circulars will rejoice over RedTag.com, which offers rock-bottom prices on brand-name items like Krups kitchenware, Sony telephones, and collectible Barbies. Stop by daily for clearance deals—the savings are significant and the selection changes constantly, so it pays to be persistent.

Andy's Garage Sale www.andysgarage.com
You'll find an odd assortment of stuff at Andy's, like you would at a traditional garage sale. But unlike the sale on your neighbor's front lawn, you won't have to get up at the crack of dawn to get the good stuff. Everything offered on the site is new, and while you'll have to tolerate the garish site design while you shop, the jewelry, tools, kid's toys, and electronics are always dirt cheap. You may not find what you were looking for, but you will find something.

Across the Board Discounts www.atbdiscounts.com
Feeling cheated by the prices at your local mall? Stop in to Across the Board Discounts and get, well, across the board discounts. You can save money on jewelry, bicycles, housewares, electronics, toys, gifts, and stained glass at this decidedly low-tech site. The selection is totally unpredictable, so don't expect to find anything particular.

Campus estore www.campusestore.com
Miscellany headquarters for students. The rather eclectic range of items at Campus estore—from tape recorders to bath towels, school supplies, and framed posters—is geared toward college students who missed the care package from Mom.

AS ON TV www.asontv.com
It slices, it dices, it cleans your curtains and whitens your teeth! Where can you find this amazing product for a limited time only? Only at AS ON TV, where you'll find all those nifty gadgets, doohickeys, and special offers you've seen advertised on the boob tube. Want to vacuum-pack your food? Try the FoodSaver. Need to fix a button? The Buttoneer makes it a breeze. And if you just caught the tail end of your favorite infomercial but missed the number to call, use AS ON TV's handy search engine to find exactly what you're looking for.

Electronics

ROXY.com www.roxy.com Ⓢ
"Where's the 'on' button?" "How the heck do I record an outgoing message?" "Doesn't this phone come with a cord?" If these are questions you tend to ask after buying an electronic gadget, make it a practice to shop at ROXY.com. Not only will customer service help you find just the right VCR, they'll tell you how it works after it's been delivered.

Everything Wireless www.everythingwireless.com
No strings attached—Everything Wireless is one-stop shopping for just about anything without a cord. Cellular phones, PDAs, satellite communication, two-way radios, and all the fixins that go along with them are available here. The site can also help you select a service plan that's compatible with your requirements.

Point.com www.point.com Ⓒ Ⓓ Ⓢ
Don't have a cell phone yet? Point.com's comprehensive and content-rich site (which includes an 800-term glossary) should inspire even confirmed Luddites to join the 21st century, with comparison charts of more than 4,000 service plans, phone prices, and all kinds of tips and tricks—like how to screen calls and track battery strength on your new Nokia. And yes, you can buy a phone and sign up for service here. Choose from Ericsson, Motorola, Nokia, and Sony, among others.

800.COM www.800.com Ⓒ Ⓢ
Discriminating e-shoppers will feel right at home at 800.com, where they'll have access to side-by-side comparisons, buying tips, and discussion groups for purchasing electronics. All the big names are here, including Fisher, Motorola, and Aiwa; our search for digital cameras pulled up 40 choices, plus customer reviews of each product, buying tips, a glossary of terms, and a digital camera chat session. All this and live customer service to boot—800.com is one e-store that knows what it's doing.

Crutchfield Electronics www.crutchfield.com Ⓒ Ⓢ

Low-cost shipping, tech-savvy customer service, the best brands in the consumer electronics industry. Simply put, Crutchfield Electronics is a terrific store. Why shop elsewhere when Crutchfield has car audio systems, home theater equipment, and all kinds of accessories backed up by a great tech-support team? Be sure to check out the Scratch and Dent section, where you can buy merchandise with cosmetic imperfections at reduced prices.

SoundDomain.com www.sounddomain.com

Who cares if your car stalls, skids, or slides? The real questions is, does it rock? The stereos, speakers, and electronic doodads at SoundDomain.com can make your car's sound system the envy (or terror) of the neighborhood. Browse for a Blaupunkt, Alpine, JVC, or Panasonic CD player, pick up some crunchy Boss subwoofers (essential for rattling pedestrian teeth), or talk shop with aficionados in the chat rooms.

J&R www.jandr.com

If a few of your favorite things include windowless portable air conditioners, Brother fax machines, Apple iBooks, and Yamaha sound systems, skip on over to J&R, whose inventory can't be beat. In addition to all the electronic gizmos that make your heart go pitter-pat, there's also a hefty list of software and music here. You'll have 30 days to exchange or return most items, but you may want to call the toll-free number to get the scoop on your specific purchase.

Circuit City www.circuitcity.com

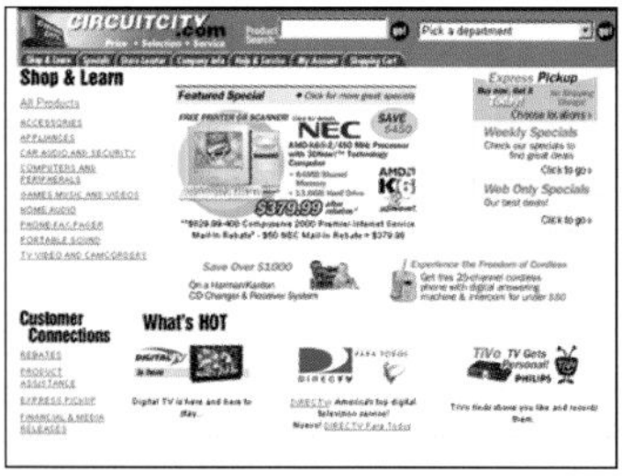

Instead of trusting some slimy salesperson to pick out your sound system, head for this electronics Web site. It's got a Shop & Learn feature that will quiz you about your needs and then spit out a list of products that meet your demands. Don't panic if some of the technical jargon has got you muddled; there's a handy dandy glossary to give you the lowdown on everything from VCR+ to USB ports. Puts the power of decision-making squarely in the consumer's hands.

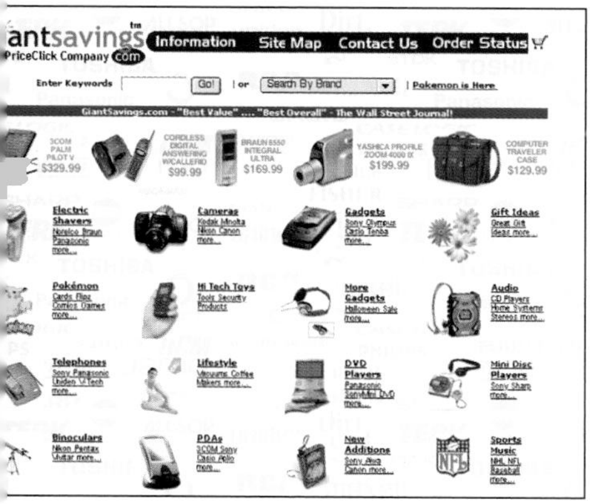

GiantSavings www.giantsavings.com
With an inventory like this, you'd jolly well better get giant savings. In addition to the standard electronics for home and office, you'll find products here to suit any need: smoke out speed traps, remove unsightly body hair, spy on your spouse, or pelt the neighbor's car with paint balls. There aren't any side-by-side comparisons here; come to GiantSavings to browse the selection (nice, large pictures make it easy) and search for deals.

Supreme Video+Electronics www.supremevideo.com
Welcome to one of the best video and electronics sites on the Web. Whatever you need to shoot a photo, record a video, play a DVD, or edit your own work, the tools are here. High-quality, brand-name items and detailed specs on each make shopping for equipment almost erotic. And this is no warehouse electronics store staffed by pubescent teens; live salespeople wait to walk you through your purchase in online chat sessions (during normal business hours).

etown.com www.etown.com ⓒ ⓓ ⓢ
Now this is what an electronics Web site should look like! Make no mistake, though: etown.com is more than just a pretty face. Brimming with up-to-the-minute news stories, expert reviews, and easy-to-follow tutorials, etown.com makes buying camcorders, cell phones, DTVs, and surround-sound stereos almost pleasurable. Before you click through the checkout page, be sure to read the return policy for the specific etown.com dealer you're purchasing from. You may decide that a higher price from a dealer with a money-back guarantee is better than a cheaper model with a 15% restocking fee.

etown.com

The Sharper Image www.sharperimage.com
For the person on your list who has everything—or just wants everything. Magic Q Balls, a pocket-sized wide-screen TV, and massagers for every occasion (and body part) are just some of the mind-blowing gifts you'll find at The Sharper Image. Some of the prices might make you swallow hard, but there is a goodly amount of merchandise that won't break your bank account.

Global Mart www.globe-mart.com

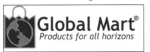

Consumers with foresight will appreciate the varied selection at Global Mart: Where else can a parent buy an electric guitar for Janey's 16th birthday and a power saw as insurance against midnight jam sessions? In addition to the run-of-the-mill computers, camcorders, and kitchen appliances available at every other electronics site, you'll find such diverse items as home weather stations, portable solar panels, and high-powered metal detectors.

cameraworld.com www.cameraworld.com

Shutterbugs of the world unite. Though the name is a bit of a misnomer (the company offers all sorts of home electronics, not just cameras), this is the place to stock up on digital, video, and 35mm cameras from brands like Canon, Nikon, Fugi, and Samsung. Amateurs will benefit from the Creative Photography tutorial, which teaches everything from developing your own style to taking great wedding photos. Specialized shopping at its finest.

DAMARK www.damark.com

Sifting through this hodgepodge of consumer electronics isn't easy, but the persistence may pay off in your pocketbook. The everything-but-the-kitchen-sink catalog retailer offers computers, snowboards, jewelry, metal detectors, and everything in between, usually from lesser-known brands. If you're looking for even deeper discounts, dip into the Outlet Store. Happy hunting!

iGadget.com www.igadget.com

Go, go iGadget.com. This site's wide assortment of gizmos includes caller ID boxes, lighters, and telescopes, as well as big-ticket audio and video equipment. Replace that electric razor you've been meaning to throw out or browse the unique gifts for a mechanically minded friend. (You must know someone who needs an electro-stun fly swatter.) Be sure to double-check your order at checkout—14 days is the limit for returns and you'll be charged a 15% restocking fee to boot.

Erotica

xandria.com www.xandria.com

Simply stated, xandria.com is sex toys, massage oils, audio and video tapes, books, and a smattering of lingerie, searchable by benefit (even toys for people with disabilities). The Sex Education section includes a handy glossary of anatomical terms and illustrations. One hundred percent satisfaction, guaranteed? Sounds good to us. You can even return anything that doesn't, uh, work.

Good Vibrations www.goodvibes.com (d) (s)

Treating hysteria among housewives was the original function of the vibrator when it was invented in 1869. Since then, better technology and broader minds have done away with the eggbeater-like contraptions of yore, and Good Vibrations has become *the* place to buy them. Don't miss the vibrator museum while you're here; you'll get a little bit of history and a new appreciation of batteries.

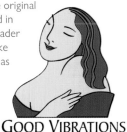

Toys in Babeland www.babeland.com

Timid shoppers: breathe easy. This woman-owned, woman-operated site will make your first foray into erotic shopping a breeze. The Vibe Coach takes you step by step through the selection process, while founders Rachel and Claire are accessible in a Q&A forum to answer any questions you might have. Gift registry is available for shoppers who are especially forthright with friends and family.

Condomania www.condomania.com (c)

With words like "polyurethane" and "Nonoxynol-9" floating around, safe sex can seem a lot like a chemistry exam. Enter Condomania's Condom Wizard, a wizened animation that will help you find just the right lube, dental dam, or rubber, be it plain, ribbed, or even chocolate flavored. Same-day shipping, if you get your order in by 2 p.m.

Flowers

Flowerbud.com www.flowerbud.com (d)

Until other online florists pick up on the idea that there's a market for elegant, beautifully arranged floral bouquets, Flowerbud.com has got that market cornered. Stop here for arrangements that whisper, "I picked this just for you" instead of screaming, "This was the best they had for under $30." If you really want to bowl someone over, enroll them in the Flowers 365 Club, which will send your beloved fresh flowers once a week for an entire year.

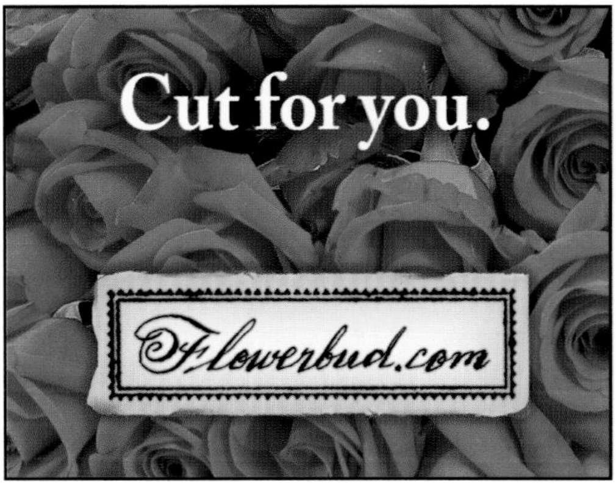

FTD.COM www.ftd.com

FTD, or Florists' Telegraph Delivery, may not do much business by morse code anymore, but we're betting their online sales are booming. Take your pick of flowers, fruit baskets, balloons, and gourmet snacks—they've got the art of seasonal gift-giving down to a science. They'll even provide a heart-warming message for you to plagiarize for your card.

1-800-FLOWERS.COM
www.1800flowers.com (s)
A pepper plant for a spicy surprise, a container of tulip bulbs for a delayed bouquet ... This site's motto, "flowers are just the beginning," isn't frivolous lip service. Check out the gift reminder service and the Giftology feature to search for presents according to the recipient's astrological sign. The company promises that their flowers will live for at least a week; a complaint eChatline is ready 24-7 in case they don't.

flowersandgifts.com www.flowersandgifts.com
Any site that has Stuff for Me! listed as an occasion has a place in our heart. Whether you're a cash-strapped college student or just stuck for gift ideas, this Web site has the plant life and the pecan loaf you've been looking for. While the floral arrangements aren't particularly distinctive, they are tastefully arranged and priced to move. The customer service chatline is hit or miss, so if you have a burning question you may get singed.

FLOWER.COM www.flower.com
B.Y.O.B. is the order of the day at FLOWER.COM—build your own bouquet, that is. You pick the exact combination of container and flowers for your arrangement—pack it with peonies or stuff it with sunflowers. Florally challenged folks can select a prearranged design instead, so you know exactly what you're sending your secretary for her birthday. Don't know her exact address? FLOWER.COM can help you locate it through their national address database.

FreshFlowerSource.com www.freshflowersource.com
With a flower industry standard of six days from cut to customer, you never know whether the roses you ordered will arrive dried or alive. Not so with FreshFlowerSource.com. This site cuts its flowers every morning and ships them to you within 24 hours for prime freshness. Orders go out by FedEx, so the chance of carrier mishap is slim; if your flowers don't arrive in "beautiful condition," FreshFlowerSource.com will replace the bouquet or refund your money.

Food & Drink

Cooking.com www.cooking.com (c) (d) (s)
Weekly menu planners, holiday menus at a glance, recipes for international food, and feature articles are just the tip of the iceberg at Cooking.com, which is also a giant kitchen accessory superstore. Find everything from tablecloths to barbeques to cake pans and food processors in the great shopping section, which features searches by product, brand name, or price range. The site could inspire even the cooking-impaired to slip on some oven mitts and get baking.

Peapod www.peapod.com

Skip dealing with squeaky grocery carts and dodging pyramids of canned peas—unless, of course, you enjoy running the grocery store obstacle course. Peapod will deliver the items on your shopping list directly to your home at the time you designate, at prices only slightly higher than your neighborhood grocer's. Fresh produce, meat, and bakery goods (hand-selected by Peapod's trained shoppers) are only available for delivery in eight metropolitan areas, but suburban folk can have non-perishables delivered by UPS.

CookExpress.com www.cookexpress.com

For those dinner dates where mac and cheese simply won't cut it, log on to CookExpress.com. Give them a day's notice and they'll deliver all the ingredients for a full-course gourmet meal—washed, sliced, chopped, and prepped so you can cook and serve it steaming hot in 30 minutes. They provide the food, cooking directions, and nutritional information for scrumptious entrees like Apricot Chicken with Crème Fraîche Smashed Potatoes. You provide the wine, candlelight, and charm. Easy!

Balducci.com
www.balducci.com

Live a life of (small) luxury with smoked sturgeon, caviar, or Italian biscotti from this Greenwich Village institution, originally a grocery stand founded in 1915 by (who else?) Louis "Pop" Balducci. Order a full-course lobster meal or take your inspiration from the recipe of the day; the descriptions of the foods are detailed and mouthwatering. But be sure to read the shipping and ordering information carefully. Shipping rates vary by the type of food purchased, and certain foods can't be shipped seven days a week.

Beverages Direct www.beveragesdirect.com

File this one under adventures in carbonation. Unique and hard-to-find sodas, juices, teas, and waters (most of which you've never heard of) are the specialty at Beverages Direct. Why drink Coke when you can swig Green Apple Soda, Jamaican Ginger Beer, FuFu Berry, or Blue Bubble Gum? You can also score energy drinks like Bawls, Red Bull, and Water Joe, each with enough caffeine to fuel a marathon night of site-surfing.

GourmetMarket.com www.gourmetmarket.com

Gustatory goodies like antipasti olives, fig cherry jam, and even a complete Texas barbecue dinner await at GourmetMarket.com, a gift-oriented gourmet site that sells breads, cheeses, fruits, jams, and desserts, among other things. Many of the foods here are hand-selected by guest chefs and experts. (Be sure to browse the wine section.) One beef: the navigation and search features are clunky—pulldown menus in the cheese section (for example) let you search by region and price but not by type of cheese.

HICKORYFARMS.com www.hickoryfarms.com
Don't just send Christmas fruitcakes this year; at HICKORYFARMS.com, you can take your pick from beef and cheese baskets, candy and nut gift boxes, and specialty meats and seafood. Or, if you're running short on time, order your Christmas turkey online, accompanied by a tasty pumpkin cheesecake. Really, there's no reason to leave your house at all!

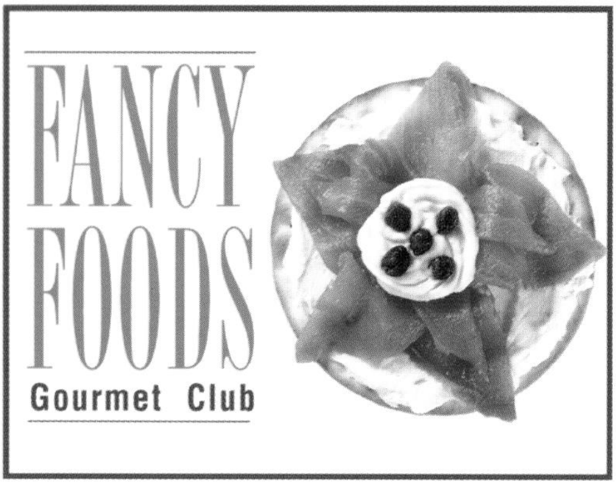

Fancy Foods Gourmet Club
www.ffgc.com
Called "the Tiffany's of food clubs," Fancy Foods Gourmet Club lets you buy all the edibles for your next formal dinner party. From caviar to goose liver mousse to chocolates and desserts, it's all here, complete with a handy marking system that tells you which items are heart-healthy and which are kosher.

Onlinefood.com www.onlinefood.com
Culinary adventures await at Onlinefood.com, where Middle Eastern, German, Italian, Asian, kosher, and Spanish foods share the shelves. With more than 50,000 items from around the globe (baklava to bamboo leaves), you can plan a theme dinner or mix and match. Who says marinated cactus doesn't go with udon?

A.K.A. Gourmet www.akagourmet.com
Feeling generous? Give Jelly Bellies, lemon butter cookies, Ghirardelli chocolates (and more) in an overstuffed gift basket from A.K.A. Gourmet. This is the place to go for delectable and beautifully packaged holiday and birthday baskets. The menu bar is organized by occasion, so you'll know exactly where to click for Hanukkah or new-baby gifts. They'll even throw in a personalized card for free.

Webvan www.webvan.com (c) (d) (s)
A dinner of succulent, herb-laden turkey meatballs, linguine, Caesar salad, and red wine tastes especially good when you don't have to cook it. Webvan is grocery shopping for enlightened San Franciscans, offering pre-prepared meals as well as your usual produce, deli meat, and baked goods. You can schedule the delivery (by van, not by mail) to arrive within a 30-minute window. If only this service were available in more cities!

Harry and David www.harryanddavid.com
Harry and David can make a pear sound more like a slice of heaven than a piece of fruit. Besides impressive-looking fruit, they also sell chocolates, cheese, and nuts, available separately or in gift baskets. If you want to take a bite before ordering, check out the store locator and hope there's one near you. No returns (of course) but they promise you'll enjoy it or you're entitled to a full refund.

wine.com www.wine.com (s)
An equal-opportunity site for the expert who knows what he wants and the novice who just needs something he can bring, unembarrassed, to a party. With more than 30 varieties of vino and a democratic pricing guide, you'll definitely find a bottle within your budget at wine.com. Not sure what food goes with what wine? Try the merlot and gourmet chocolate combination.

Dean & Deluca www.deandeluca.com (d)
Astronomically priced (but gastronomically unparalleled) food from the SoHo grocer of legend. The site peddles luxury basics like truffles, chocolate, caviar, and fine cheeses, as well as D&D's own specialty items (almond flour and dried Morel mushrooms, among others). Nothing can stop your mouth from watering, but the price tags will keep you from splurging (balsamic vinegar for $175?).

Starbucks.com www.starbucks.com
Jonesing for a cup of joe? Head to Starbucks.com. They can't send you a steaming hot latte, but they will send you beans by the pound and tea, chocolate, or biscotti to go with them. For fun, try the Coffee Taste Matcher, which lets you know what kind of coffee drinker you really are.

GreatCoffee.com www.greatcoffee.com (c) (s)
An awesome site for people who are very particular about their coffee beans—down to the type of grind, flavor, shape, and color. Choose from green beans, estates, espressos, dark roasts, or blends, and order an espresso machine to boot. It's worth checking out the weekly specials, which occasionally include free shipping, and the reviews and recommendations at the linked CoffeeReview site.

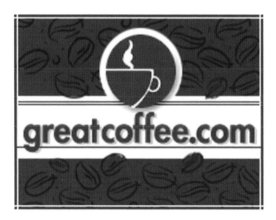

TAVOLO

Tavolo www.tavolo.com ⓒ

Have a special occasion coming up? Here's our advice: preheat your oven, dial up Tavolo, and try not to get batter on the iMac. With cookbooks, kitchenware, and buying guides, you won't find a better resource for cooking gourmet. Use the recipe channel for meal suggestions, preparation instructions, and a categorized shopping list. Then shop their specialty foods to buy the ingredients you'll need. Apricot and White Chocolate Brownies are only minutes away.

ChefShop.com www.chefshop.com ⓢ

You're a whiz at Miracle Whip, but Julia Child you're not. Fake it for your next dinner party with ChefShop.com's assortment of fancy foods, ranging from premade marinara sauce to plum pudding and biscotti. You'll also appreciate the site's advice columns and tips, product reviews, and seasonal articles on fixing a feast, whatever the occasion.

ChefShop.com

WholeFoods.com www.wholefoods.com

That Twinkie may tickle your tastebuds, but it'll leave your body wanting. Feed your nutritional needs with natural and organic canned foods, snacks, entrees, and bulk basics from WholeFoods.com. The site offers green versions of items found in your local grocery store, including environmentally sound cleaning products, toys, and batteries. Shopping online requires (free) registration first.

Food.com www.food.com ⓓ

Welcome to the Internet's takeout and delivery service. At Food.com, you can access menus from restaurants in your area and order dinner for delivery in an hour or less. Though the selection varies from city to city, you're sure to find a refreshing alternative to pizza and Chinese among the 12,000 restaurants listed.

Liquor.com www.liquor.com ⓒ

Want to impress at your next cocktail party? Liquor.com lets you personalize a bottle of champagne by putting your own message on the label. The site is full of quirky offerings like this, plus links to the Libation Library and Ask the Bartender. Of course, an enormous range of booze is available, from a $14 bottle of tequila to a $799 bottle of Dom Perignon. Just be sure to scroll down when shopping: prices are listed in descending order.

NetGrocer.com www.netgrocer.com ⓢ

Finding items in the grocery store can make you feel like the object of the stock boy's personal vendetta. End the insanity with NetGrocer.com's ShopFast feature. You enter your shopping list, NetGrocer.com matches it with items that are in stock (indicating which items are on sale), then ships them to you by FederalExpress. The site even saves your list to make your next shopping trip easier. Victory is yours.

Godiva.com www.godiva.com ⓓ

Chocolate: the fifth food group. Get your recommended daily intake at Godiva.com, the best place to shop for the brand's infamously decadent treats. Choices range from simple all-milk boxes to 30-piece truffle assortments–the Chocolate Guide will help you decipher what's in each one before you bite. Godiva ice cream, liqueur, and kosher selections can be found in the specialty items section.

Ben & Jerry's Gifts by Mail store.benjerry.com

Divine bovine or just plain dairy know-how; either way, Ben and Jerry make some incredible ice cream. Now, thanks to a little dry ice, you can have it delivered conveniently (albeit expensively) to your door. Read the descriptions of their 30+ flavors to find out what crazy ingredients go into the ones you love (chocolate fish!), then select which you want to send. A word of warning: too much Ben & Jerry's, and Chubby Hubby will be more than just a flavor.

CandyDirect.com www.candydirect.com

Four out of five dentists recommend not going anywhere near CandyDirect.com, but don't let a little thing like cavities stop you. CandyDirect.com has your fix of Jujyfruits, Butterfingers, and more, plus specialty candy like Aquarium Squeeze Pops. You'll be buying in bulk, but the prices are roughly what they would be at the corner store ($24.93 for 24 King Size Baby Ruths). Stock your pantry for Halloweens to come.

OmahaSteaks.com www.omahasteaks.com

Just another link in the food chain. OmahaSteaks.com can send you nearly any type of dinner meat (sans fins)–order prime beef, poultry, or lamb. Chefs should also visit the cookbook section or recipe exchange for detailed instructions on how to prepare their purchases.

Fulton Street Lobster and Seafood Co. www.fultonstreet.com ⓢ

New York's legendary fish market flash-freezes their super-fresh fish, rock lobster tails, and crab legs, and will send them to you by overnight FedEx. You can also purchase soups, desserts, and seafood pasta here, as well as live lobsters, should a particularly special occasion arise. There is a $9.99 flat rate for shipping and handling, so go ahead and stock up.

Nirvana Chocolates www.nirvanachocolates.com ⓒ ⓓ

For anyone who dreads biting into a cherry liqueur chocolate, this site's Select Your Own Chocolate feature is a must-surf. The service lets you fill up a customized box with your choice from more than 30 delectable options. Also check out the History of Chocolate link and Nirvana Chocolates' tips for keeping your morsels in top shape.

Caesar's Palate www.caesarspalate.com ⓒ ⓓ

When the closest you've come to an opulent meal is last week's Caesar salad, it's time to splurge on some truly rich food. This site has luxury classics like smoked fish, caviar, chocolate, and pâté, as well as some more unusual items (think squid ink and wild boar). If all you have to serve your caviar on is paper plates, there is also a small but attractive selection of settings and silverware. Complete refund for returns within 30 days.

Games

Gamestop www.gamestop.com

Carpal tunnel factor: 10. You'll wish you'd worn a wrist brace after visiting Gamestop, home of more PC and video games than you can shake a joystick at. There are separate game areas for PCs, Sega Dreamcast, Nintendo 64, Sony Playstation, and Game Boy, and there's even a respectable Macintosh section (hallelujah!). Downloadable demos will help you decide if a game is worth your attention, and should you get your Diddy Kong stuck in a tree, one of the many official strategy guides can help you out.

Game Cave www.gamecave.com ⓒ

With a name like Game Cave, you might think you're entering the Dark Ages of computer gaming. Not so. Game Cave has got all the cutting-edge video games, in addition to soundtracks (nothing like the main theme of "Final Fantasy VII" to set a mood), action figures, and wall scrolls. Top it all off with respectable prices and an inexhaustible selection, and you've got a gaming resource fit for the 21st century.

EBWorld.com www.ebworld.com

Finding your way through some game sites can feel like an epic saga. EBWorld.com's well-organized design makes it easy to navigate the monster selection of games for PCs, PlayStation, Nintendo 64, Game Boy, Macintosh, and, of course, Pokémon. Check New Releases for the latest games on the market.

bargainbins www.bargainbins.com

A virtual dime store for digital media, bargainbins carries a fair selection of games, educational programs, utilities, and miscellany, priced well under retail value. Check the New Items Page for frequent updates or the Under $9.95 page for a random selection of dirt cheap software. Dig around–there are some gems to be found here.

eGames www.egames.com

Parents can rest easy with this site's exclusively family-friendly selection of games. The puzzles, brain teasers, shooting galleries, and adventure games here focus on strategy rather than guts and gore, with graphics that rival their more violent counterparts. Some are available at a discount by download, others come in software packs or on CD-ROM. Keep an eye out for special offerings like the Games for Girls pack.

UGOdirect www.ugodirect.com (c) (d)
Choosing a game can be at least as rigorous as actually playing one. UGO's tempting online shop lets you search games by platform, keyword, or interest (sports, sci-fi, family, etc.) and provides a compatibility function to help you find coordinated joysticks, control pads, and video and sound cards. Tip for parents: check the product pages for helpful maturity labels and browse New Releases to find out what Junior wants for his birthday.

Sega www.sega.com (design)
Hedgehogs, severed heads, and all the cuddly favorites in Sega's cast of characters are on view at the company site, which is a great place to buy Dreamcast and other Sega products. You'll find the company's whole range of strangely named games ("Rippin' Riders," "Bass Fishing"), as well as consoles, controllers, and game-specific bulletin boards (for the truly devout).

Computer and Video Games www.computerandvideogames.com (c)
News, reviews, and previews await at this specialty e-zine for digital diversions. With so much information available in the current edition and in archived past issues, it would be a crime to buy without browsing here first. See how many stars their staff gave the latest copy of "Quake" or keep track of what's hitting stores in the coming months. The site is useful for shoppers worldwide but is geared toward British gamers.

Gifts & Cards

GiftCertificates.com www.giftcertificates.com
Don't panic when you draw the computer guy in the next Secret Santa lottery; instead, head for GiftCertificates.com. Unlike similar services, this site helps you search vendors by category, occasion, recipient, or zip code. If you still can't decide what Mr. or Ms. Mysterian would like, pick up a Super Certificate, which can be redeemed at more than 200 merchants, including Banana Republic, iBeauty.com, Eddie Bauer, or Benihana.

GiftCertificates.com™

giftpoint.com www.giftpoint.com
For all those friends and relatives who promise, "I'm sure anything you get me will be just fine," there's giftpoint.com. With gift certificates that can be redeemed at hundreds of national and local stores, restaurants, and salons, this service takes the stress out of shopping for presents and lets recipients find what they want at establishments like Express, Barnes and Noble, Loews Cinemas, and Footlocker.

CarePackages.com www.carepackages.com
Chances are, you know a bookworm who could use some snacks and a little Visine, or a camper with a mean craving for Chips Ahoy. CarePackages.com takes the legwork out of sending treats by offering fantastic, pre-packaged boxes for students, sweethearts, or anyone else needing a boost. The site will also help you put together a personalized package, should the recipient have especially discerning tastes.

Propagangsta www.propagangsta.com

Though the name sounds like a lesson in homeboy etiquette, Propagangsta is actually a gift shop with a crazy selection of items for the trend-inclined. The inflatable furniture, hipster watches, plastic wine racks, and other funky, fashionable wares here are heavy on design and light on price. Don't leave before you register a wish list—just in case anyone you give to wants to return the favor.

Hallmark.com www.hallmark.com (c)

From the company that invented gift wrap (no, really) comes a handy site for all the occasions you didn't even know existed. Send a free e-card to commemorate a new pet, observe Sweetest Day (October 21), or mark the start of a school year. Of course, Hallmark.com can also help you celebrate more traditional holidays with a variety of flowers, gifts, and ornaments.

Violet www.violet.com (d) (s)

You waited until the last minute to get your quirky boss a birthday present and now you're in for it. Race to Violet, where the gift finder takes phrases like "I'm in trouble if I don't get a hip gift for my artistic boss" and spits back a stellar assortment of appropriate items. With free shipping on orders of $25 or more, free gift wrap, and a handwritten card, you can consider your job saved.

Sparks.com www.sparks.com (c)

When Sparks.com says they have cards for any occasion, they're not kidding. These cool paper cards can be shipped to you or sent directly to anyone you want, complete with a personal message. You can also include a gift certificate from the nearly 40 companies that are featured here.

redENVELOPE
GIFTS ONLINE

RedEnvelope
www.redenvelope.com (d) (s)

According to Asian tradition, the most cherished presents come in a red envelope. No doubt anyone who receives an envelope containing one of this site's fine items will feel the same. Get gorgeous candles, sweets, tools, and other eclectic wares for the explorer, host, handyman, or epicure in your life. If you have a problem, log on and chat live with a service representative any time, day or night.

MakeHisDay.com www.makehisday.com

Shop at MakeHisDay.com for the man who appreciates fine cuff links, watches, and leather goods. A Kenneth Cole watch, a Troika shave set, or a Bruno Magli wallet can be bought, wrapped, and shipped in four clicks flat—perfect for last-minute Father's Day gifts.

Flooz www.flooz.com
Cooler than paper gift certificates and classier than cash, Flooz are online "gift dollars" that can be redeemed at a long list of online stores. Participating sites include TowerRecords.com, Skechers, Art.com, and iGadget.com; the list is growing. A helpful customer service FAQ page and a toll-free number make this already convenient shopping experience even smoother. Hey, Whoopi Goldberg floozes; shouldn't you?

iParty www.iparty.com
You slaved over the cake but forgot the crepe paper? IParty has supplies for a thousand different occasions–pick your theme and the site will shower you with choices of favors, cake decorations, balloons, and trimmings. It also has separate sections for the most popular kids' party themes, should Junior demand Barney, Pooh, or Scooby-Doo. You will have 30 days to return everything except seasonal merchandise–so don't cancel that Christmas party if you've already ordered supplies.

Evite.com www.evite.com
Paper invitations may be going by the wayside with e-mail around, but that doesn't mean that all social etiquette is lost! Evite.com is an online invitation service that helps organize the time, date, place, and RSVPs for your business or casual event. It's free, but registration is required. What a terrific idea!

Lanac.com www.lanac.com
Feather your new nest with the best or inject a little extra luxury into someone else's life. Lanac.com's elegant flatware, crystal, china, and jewelry (from names like Lenox, Lladro, and Noritake) are perfect for elegant corporate and wedding gifts. Need a housewarming present fast? Express shopping can help you locate a gift under $100. Note: you'll have better luck with the toll-free number than the live chat option.

Send.com www.send.com (S)
For the *GQ* man in your life, Send.com can help you locate cigars, scotch, golf equipment, and–if you're feeling generous–luxury autos. Send him (or her) to a luxury spa, or just buy enough good wine for the two of you to celebrate. Shipping is always free–and gifts are sent express delivery.

Archie McPhee www.mcphee.com (C)
A boxing nun is hard to beat–unless, of course, you have the boxing Godzilla or another boxing puppet from Archie McPhee. Specializing in the wacky, weird, and wonderful, this Seattle store is the place to get a rooster alarm clock that crows or a sarcastic 8-ball (Yeah, right!). You can also play online games or request a catalog. Free gift with every order (and chances are, it's something slimy).

AutoRomantic.com www.autoromantic.com ©

If your idea of a great gift for your wife is a blender, you owe it to your marriage to stop by AutoRomantic.com. Not only does this Web site have terrific gift ideas, it also has lists of romantic things to do (we won't give any away). There's also a personal profile system that can help you find exactly the right present for your dream gal.

Warner Bros. Studio Store www.wbstore.com

It's the dubba-dubba-WB! That singing frog is thankfully absent from this network's site, but anything Warner Bros.-related can definitely be found here. Buy a Looney Tunes menorah, a DC Comics Batman boot stocking, or just browse the bridal accessories. That's right, bridal accessories. The site is a bit cluttered, but with so much weird stuff to buy, you'll quickly move beyond the mess.

The Nature Company www.natureco.com

Get back to nature! Or at least bring nature into your home with unusual gifts and earthy products from The Nature Company. Their online store is full of funky and fanciful wares, like well-designed bird feeders and glow-in-the-dark stars for your bedroom ceiling. You can also request a catalog or use the store-locator to find a Nature Company near you.

Americangreetings.com www.americangreetings.com ©

Forgot your anniversary again? Register at Americangreetings.com for a handy reminder service that will guarantee you'll never have to pick up one of those "Oops! I forgot" cards again. There's also a selection of gifts to bribe your loved one with, including chocolates, gourmet foods, and educational games. Free membership also entitles you to create, personalize, and print greeting cards in your very own home.

Card Star www.cardstar.com

Beneath its drab design lurks the soul of a useful and unique e-commerce site. Card Star features greeting cards for all sorts of business occasions. Themes include prospecting for business, follow up, decision making, client service, referrals, thank you notes, and financial advisors. If you're a small business person who wants to make a good impression, stop here.

Spencergifts.com www.spencergifts.com

It says something about a site when one of its top ten cool gifts is a remote control fart machine. But Spencer Gifts is renowned for humor that is, to put it kindly, sophomoric. Come here for kitschy inflatable furniture, lava lamps, music collectibles (gaze in awe upon the KISS bookends), as well as an assortment of bachelor and bachelorette party accessories. Daring types should stop in at the Spice Up Your Life section, which features various naughty knickknacks, from body paint to erotic board games.

BravoGifts.com www.bravogifts.com
Buying a business gift is always a tricky proposition, which is what makes this well-designed Web site such a godsend. If you can't decide what to buy from the wide range of categories offered here (office accessories, gourmet food, flowers, etc.), you can always head to the Suggestions page. The beautiful gift boxes add that special little touch that puts this store over the top.

TheGift.com www.thegift.com
Looking for an inexpensive gift? Check out TheGift.com's inspired 20 under $20 feature, which lists a bevy of ideas for the cash-strapped giver. The site also offers options for those with money to burn, including gourmet food, cut crystal, and specialty items for Him and Her. TheGift.com will wrap your present, include a personal message, and ship it right to the recipient's door.

ARTiSANgifts.com www.artisangifts.com
Featuring whimsical, one-of-a-kind art objects from over 1,500 artists and craftspeople worldwide, ARTiSANgifts.com offers gift-worthy items like handmade candles, vases, and picture frames. Your choice arrives wrapped in a silky satin bag and includes information on the artist who made it.

Fortunoff www.fortunoff.com
When you've been around for close to 80 years, as Fortunoff has, you've got to be doing something right. Selling "necessities and niceties," this retailer specializes in fine jewelry and watches, home furnishings and antique silver. "Elegance" is the word du jour here, whether you want formal china, millennium cutlery, or cultured pearls. Although not inexpensive, Fortunoff's products often carry a surprisingly reasonable price tag, but if you're really concerned, you can search by price range.

giftTree www.gifttree.com
Go beyond the traditional fruit basket for your next Christmas gift—try something a little more unusual from giftTree. The gift-basket headquarters offers a pasta dinner basket, a Chocoholic's Delight basket, and a late night snack basket, to name three. While you're here, you can also buy flowers, send a virtual card, or schedule a reminder for an upcoming occasion. The prices are a bit steep, but such is the cost of flawless gift options.

Egreetings www.egreetings.com ©
egreetings.com®
Paper cards look passé up against Egreetings' digital greeting cards. The site has a huge selection of moving, singing, blinking e-cards for traditional sentiments (Christmas, Halloween) as well as more contemporary ones (gay/lesbian, teen, etc.). Membership is free, and allows you to send cards, keep track of important addresses and dates, and keep a virtual photo album on the site. For cards with character, this hits the cyber-spot.

Cigar.com www.cigar.com
Find over 100 brands of cigars at Cigar.com, plus humidors and other cigar smoking accessories. The shop carries Cubans (like Havana Gold) as well as a few unique selections. We love their no minimum policy: If you just want to try out a new brand, you can order a single cigar instead of a whole box.

National Geographic Store www.ngstore.com
Get out of your shell and learn more about the world outside at this thorough site. Buy globes, maps, CD-ROMs, videos, or a subscription to the century-old magazine. From classic brass telescopes to an electronic star locator, the National Geographic Store has it all. Perfect if you want to see the world but can't spend your life traveling it.

Christmasplace.com www.christmasplace.com
'Tis the season but you're feeling a bit Scrooge-ish? Take a trip to Chistmasplace.com to stock up on products that will put you in the spirit. From advent calendars to stockings, fake trees, home decor, and even a giant Nativity scene, the site will make you the envy of the neighborhood.

Christmasplace·com

BloomingCookies.com www.bloomingcookies.com
If you love the idea of giving cookies but your idea of baking involves squeezing dough out of a tube, leave the baking to the pros. BloomingCookies.com has baskets of elegantly arranged cookies to commemorate any occasion (or just because). Playing off the theme of cookies as flowers (as they put it, "flours"), the folks at BloomingCookies.com seem intent on feeding you sugary delicacies. Just open up and say "Aah."

The Tech Museum Online Store store.thetech.org
Who says toys are just for kids? Browse The Tech Museum Online Store for technological gifts and gadgets from the museum dedicated to science and the Silicon Valley. Here's the place to find freeze dried astronaut food, a floating pen, or a funky disk drive clock for the geek in your life. The Tech Museum is a nonprofit organization, so it's nice to know your purchases here go toward mentoring future techno-wizards (and the rest of us).

Yaz www.yaz.com
Men who don't exactly cherish jewelry shopping will want to check out Yaz. The Yaz Shopper function uses a personality profile of the lady you're buying for to determine which of the site's contemporary jewelry she might like. iMac users beware: the site isn't set up to accommodate small screens, so you may only see half of the pages.

Discovery Channel Online Store shopping.discovery.com
A virtual general store of educational gifts, toys, and accessories, the Discovery Channel Online Store offers books, videos, CD-ROMS and assorted tools to decipher the natural world for adults and kids. You'll find learning for the ages on animals, astronomy, and all that neat stuff in between. Browse through item categories or jump down to the special sections for educators and parents.

Health

more.com www.more.com ©
Need more shampoo? More cologne? More underarm deodorant, cough medicine, condoms, cold tablets, or colostomy kits? Judging by the sheer range of products here, more.com is aptly named. The helpful Related Information section gives info on health problems as you browse; while deciding on cold and flu products, for example, you can read up on bronchitis and reishi mushrooms. The shopping cart here totals your savings as well as your bill, which will help you feel better even before the Ricola kicks in.

drugstore.com www.drugstore.com ©
Take a peek inside your medicine cabinet—then head for the Web. Drugstore.com will ship you all the bathroom basics, from cotton swabs and rubbing alcohol to surprisingly good brands of makeup, shampoos, and bath products. Compare items by brand and price, get your prescriptions filled, or read the Solutions page for information on breast health, prescription prices, and how to avoid the flu.

1-800 CONTACTS www.contacts.com
No, it's not another singles site, but rather a convenient way to order contacts directly. Just like the phone service that preceded it, the site offers simple ordering for hard, disposable, gas-permeable, and colored contacts, with substantial savings off the optician's prices. With free shipping for Internet orders and a thorough FAQ page, there's no reason not to make the switch.

healthshop.com www.healthshop.com ©
If the idea of having your habits observed 24-7 makes you wince, imagine how the Hales must feel. The typical family of four consented to have their unhealthy lifestyle overhauled by healthshop.com; you can watch the transformation on the site's Webcam. If you're inspired, shop here for all the vitamins, minerals, herbs, and homeopathic remedies you need to boost your own health. An extensive catalog of articles and a health encyclopedia are also available.

PlanetRx.com www.planetrx.com

Gone are the days of the friendly corner pharmacist, so why venture out for your medicine at all? PlanetRx.com will take your prescription, fill it, ship it for free, and remind you when you're due for a refill. Need some dental floss, Vitamin E, or waterproof mascara? Order it along with your prescription and it'll get shipped for free as well. PlanetRx.com also provides health news, product advice, and a staff pharmacist who can answer questions within 24 hours.

Shopinprivate.com www.shopinprivate.com

Ever been stared down by a cashier while trying to buy wart remover, condoms, or the perpetually embarrassing Preparation H? Shopinprivate.com carries just about everything you'd be ashamed to have in your shopping cart, including products for hygiene, illness, and hair removal. The site also has useful informational links related to each product, so you can learn how to prevent a repeat occurrence. Just make sure no one's reading over your shoulder!

eNutrition www.enutrition.com

The name may be cyber-trendy but the contents of eNutrition are solid. Each of its four categories (Weight Management, Natural Remedies, Your Health, and Vitamins) is backed up by a comprehensive group of products that will help you slim down, de-stress, or just get healthier. Breaking health news, gift baskets for fitness fanatics, and a glossary of terms from "absorption" to "yeast" round out the offerings. Shipping specials change weekly, so check back often.

DrugEmporium.com www.drugemporium.com

DrugEmporium.com's Personal Shopper will save you the wristwork of clicking around for drugs, vitamins, and personal care products—simply type in your shopping list, choose from the brands it suggests, and hit the check-out page. When you aren't in rush, check out the articles and health editorials (courtesy of drkoop.com). There's even free shipping and a discount on your first order, in case you needed yet another reason to shop here.

HealthQuick.com www.healthquick.com

Bargains, bargains, bargains. This online pharmacy promises low prices and actually delivers; our search turned up a bottle of 100-count aspirin for $1.88. Add in online coupons and specials and $15 off your first order, and you may not care that HealthQuick.com's brand variety is limited. Registration is free but required if you want to shop.

Gazoontite www.gazoontite.com ⓢ

Gazoontite fills a long-empty niche by offering products for asthma and allergy sufferers. Order items like hypo-allergenic bedding, a dust mite detection kit, and an auto air purifier to make your commute a lot less sniffly. Or treat asthmatic kids to inhaler holders in the shapes of Bart Simpson and Casper. The help of a live nurse, online between 9 a.m. and noon on weekdays, is nothing to turn your nose up at either.

Vitamins.com www.vitamins.com ⓒ

Vitamin specials, vitamin experts, vitamin encyclopedia. The sheer volume of vitamin-related content here may leave you feeling like you've ODed on C. A helpful beginner's guide starts you off right, with explanations on which pills to take for better energy, immunity, and health. If you find the same vitamins cheaper elsewhere, Vitamins.com will give them to you for free.

MotherNature.com www.mothernature.com

The common cold may not have a cure, but it does have a link. MotherNature.com lets you search for remedies by ailment, so you can pinpoint which product will help your cold symptoms, arthritis, or insomnia. For a more comprehensive cure, the site also prepackages "solution baskets," full of products designed to team up against a specific ailment. There's free shipping on orders over $50, so stock up on all the environmentally safe, non-animal tested health products you need.

SelfCare www.selfcare.com

Healer, heal thyself. This site offers some unique options for taking better care of yourself. Sections for Acupressure, Aromatherapy, Light and Sound therapy, and Magnets tell you a little bit about how each works and offer products to get you started. The site also has traditional tools, like fitness equipment and nutritional supplements, to round out your regimen. You may, however, find it difficult to negotiate the magazine-like interface.

HealthZone.com www.healthzone.com ⓒ

At HealthZone.com, zones for fitness, drugstore products, supplements, and information provide the means and know-how you need to go from flabby to fit. Buy a 90% Plus Protein Chocolate Malt while reading the latest nutritional news, or find out what diet complements your physical therapy. A discussion board and chat room are also offered for swapping tips with bodybuilders, beginners, and in-betweens.

AllHerb.com www.allherb.com ⓒ ⓓ ⓢ

Why not try an all-natural cure for whatever ails you? AllHerb.com offers a wide range of herbal medicines, as well as simple info for people just looking to explore. Search by herb, vitamin, or supplement, or enter an ailment and the site will make a suggestion. The high-quality customer service here includes free shipping, no sales tax, and a personal health page.

Home & Garden

Furniture.com www.furniture.com ⓒ ⓢ

With more than 50,000 (affordable) home furnishings on offer here, there's bound to be something to help you set up your kitchen, bath, bedroom, or home office. Want to throw together a refined sitting room? Head for the Traditional Elegance corner. Going for a more Bauhaus feel? Check out the Modern selections. Furniture.com's commitment to customer service is obvious everywhere on the site; they provide substantial information about each piece before purchase, send regular e-mail updates after purchase, and even call you on the day of delivery to ensure that someone will be home.

Stacks & Stacks
www.stacksandstacks.com

The longer you live, the more stuff you amass. Clear the clutter with storage boxes, shelving, racks, carts, and furniture from Stacks & Stacks. This comprehensive site has elegant options for organizing all those unmanageable mounds of junk; should you actually succeed in clearing some space, the site carries cleaning products as well.

Gump's www.gumps.com ⓢ

The first name in eclectic and exclusive home and garden decor since 1861. Troll for treasures with an Eastern flair, like bamboo fountains, lotus flower bowls, and Kang chests, as well as fine glass, jewelry, and stationery. A classy (and pricey) choice for bridal and corporate gifts, Gump's deserves kudos for their clearly stated privacy policy. When you make a purchase, be sure to specify if you don't want them to share your e-mail or snail mail address with other companies.

marthastewart.com www.marthastewart.com

Cooking, shopping, gardening, entertaining ... does this woman ever sleep? After silently eating your heart out over that gorgeous Connecticut farmhouse that Martha calls home, do yourself a favor and check out her Web site. You'll wonder how on earth you ever made it all these years without cake pedestals, hostess tapers, padded silk hangers, and silverware drawer liners. (Of course, Martha also offers everyday basics such as linens, towels, and dishes from the Martha Stewart Collection.) Admit it, the woman could turn a motor home into Buckingham Palace on her lunch hour.

Lillian Vernon Online www.lillianvernon.com

Hand-carved spoon cabinets, floral mixing bowls, rattan storage benches ... all those little touches that make a house a home can be found at Lillian Vernon Online, the staple for all things quaint. Try the gift guide for recommendations ranging from the useful (garden tool sets) to the decorative (family welcome signs) to the whimsical (cotton candy makers).

living.com www.living.com (c) (s)
Hands down one of the most practical interior design sources on the Net—and living.com has a store to boot. After you've finished choosing a dining set, patio table, china cabinet, or night table, head over to the Room Designer, where you can virtually arrange (and rearrange) your buys in a customized floor plan. The selection mingles classic and more contemporary pieces. Also, check living.com's magazine for heaps of advice, how-tos, and trends.

Good to be Home www.goodtobehome.com
For gift-worthy home accessories like rugs, frames, and vases, Good to be Home offers a limited selection of fresh, modern design pieces. While there's style in spades here, the customer service could stand to be beefed up; the site offers precious little information about delivery, privacy, security, and other need-to-know basics.

Restoration Hardware www.restorationhardware.com
If you're someone who likes to poke around antique shops for unique items—or just want to look like you do—you'll love Restoration Hardware. It's not your typical hardware store (unless French flyswatters, fireplace corn-poppers, and mission table lamps are your idea of hardware); you will find home accessories, gifts, lighting supplies, and an elegant but limited selection of furniture.

evolve www.evolvehome.com (d)
Funky furniture and home accents for anyone who wants their apartment to look like the set of *Friends*. This Yahoo! store carries bath accessories, bar stools, dinnerware, sofas, and more; the items are specialized, pricey ($1000+ for a rattan-and-seagrass armchair), and very cool. You will have 30 days to return merchandise (at your own expense), just in case that armchair arrives scratched or you discover that you're allergic to seagrass.

Bombay www.bombayco.com (s)
Expect high-quality reproductions of traditional furniture and home accessories from this mall, catalog, and now e-tail company. Think cavernous armoires, cunning curio cabinets, four-post canopy beds, and Queen Anne desks, most with mahogany finish and brass-plated hardware. There are also entire collections designed for bedroom, dining room, and living room, as well as for home office. Why not splurge and pick up a whole set?

Crate and Barrel www.crateandbarrel.com
Rattan storage baskets, scissor-cut centerpiece bowls, Cuisinart frozen yogurt machines ... this, my fellow Americans, is what we fought the Cold War for. Get all this classic Crate and Barrel merchandise at their great-looking e-store, which opts for a manageable selection of well-photographed products rather than hundreds of tiny pictures. Purchases are backed by solid customer service and yes, you can return merchandise to the brick-and-mortar store. Ain't capitalism grand?

Carpets Direct www.carpetsdirect.com
Carpets Direct has a really attractive selection of rag rugs, wall-to-wall carpeting, and Tibetan area rugs, for starters. The prices are dynamite (a 9-by-12-foot rug typically costs around $300, except for the pricier Himalayan models), and the designs range from handsome to breathtaking. Too bad there's no customer service to speak of (not even a company address or phone number!).

TheDormStore.com www.thedormstore.com
Ah, college: the days when futons, beanbag chairs, and stringed lights were all you needed to spell "home." All the basics are online at TheDormStore.com, right down to the incense burners and the inflatable bubble sofa. Get your gear delivered directly to your dorm room (for free), then auction it off at semester's end—the At Your School Auction will help you find a fellow student at your university to take the futon off your hands.

BrylaneHome www.brylanehome.com Ⓢ
Touting itself as "America's White Sale Catalog," BrylaneHome carries mainly bedding and towels, but it also offers dinnerware, lamps, and slip covers. The site is well-organized (you can score a new comforter in about six clicks), the stuff is affordable, and customer service is available 24-7. What else can you ask for?

PuertaBella.com
www.puertabella.com Ⓒ Ⓢ
Mediterranean casual at its best: terra-cotta decorative plates, popped tin planters, wrought-iron end tables, and aged chests; all are on the menu at PuertaBella.com. This self-billed source for "world style" carries furniture and home accessories with a hand-crafted feel. Cool feature: click on an item and the site will suggest matching pieces to go along with it. Free UPS ground shipping is just icing on the cake.

1(800)MATTRESS www.mattress.com
When you've decided that that old, sagging thing you've been sleeping on for the last five years just won't cut it anymore, hop on over to 1(800)MATTRESS, where you can order a soft, fluffy good night's sleep in a matter of seconds. The site offers King Koil and Sealy mattresses, and though information on each is limited (particularly on the King Koils), what more do you need to know than size? Your bed can be delivered in 24 hours.

CyberBath Catalogue www.baths.com
If you're shopping for bathroom and kitchen fixtures, be sure to dial up CyberBath Catalogue, which has an impressive stock of faucets, toilets, shower fittings, and water filtration systems. This simple, low-tech Web site has some very good bargains, though products are organized by brand, making it difficult for non-plumbers to browse.

Hardware.com www.hardware.com ©

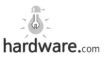

Don't know the difference between a Phillips and a standard screwdriver? Check out Hardware.com, which has all the equipment and none of the attitude of your local tool store. In addition to nifty merchandise like charcoal grills, wallpaper kits, and cordless drills, this site also has a helpful Lifestyles Buys feature to direct you to must-haves for the home, garden, or garage.

iCelebrate.com www.icelebrate.com ©

If you'd like to have an old-fashioned (or newfangled) holiday and aren't sure where to begin, look up iCelebrate.com. It's got everything from Halloween costumes to Christmas luminaries and Valentine cards. Besides the tons of cool merchandise, this site is jam-packed with recipes, crafts, and decorating ideas to make your festivities extra special. Learn how to make colorful turkey place cards, to prepare a witch's brew, and to decorate a Victorian Christmas tree all in one blow.

HomePortfolio www.homeportfolio.com ©

Wonder what your dream house could look like? With HomePortfolio, you'll never have trouble explaining what you want to interior decorators again. While you can't actually purchase items at this site, you can browse some of the most stylish home furnishings you've ever seen, rate them ("love it," "like it," "not my style"), and save them to your own personal portfolio. Nearly everything here is decidedly upscale (wingchairs start at around $1,000), but your living room will never be the same again.

GoodHome.com www.goodhome.com ©

We love the concept: GoodHome.com lets you browse through 45 fully decorated rooms (grouped by style: urban, contemporary, English country, etc.). You can order an entire room (right down to the candles), or just buy one piece at a time. Enter the decorating studio to custom-design rooms by choosing your own colors for walls and fabrics. An impressive tool that's totally fun to use.

MyHome.com www.myhome.com

MyHome.com is simply bursting with accessories to turn your shabby studio into a cozy hideaway. There's no furniture here, just small accessories like vanity shelves for your bathroom and decorative boxes for your desk. If you're not sure how to put it all together, head for the Rooms by Design section, where various decorators demonstrate how to mix and match merchandise for a fabulous effect.

Kitchen & Home www.kitchenandhome.com

Make your kitchen a place to be proud of. Kitchen & Home carries lots of useful and elegant kitchen tools, as well as furniture, flatware, glasses, and linens. If you're planning an outdoor feast, score everything from food covers to picnic baskets here. Brand-name products, solid service, money-back guarantee.

Illuminations www.illuminations.com Ⓒ

ILLUMINATIONS.COM™
LIVING BY CANDLELIGHT

Think you know all there is to know about candles? Think again. Illuminations has plenty to teach you about the art of burning candles, and the site carries hundreds of cool candles for sale. After one visit to the birthday candles section, you'll never subject your child to banal grocery-store wicks again.

doitbest.com www.doitbest.com Ⓒ

doitbest.com
world's largest hardware store

The handyperson's paradise. Anything, absolutely anything, you could conceivably need in the way of hardware is available on this site—tools, housewares, building materials, paint and electrical supplies, animal vaccines, car tires, and even Christmas tree decorations. Build it, fix it, improve it, or tear it apart—doitbest.com's how-to encyclopedia will show you how.

Widerview Village www.widerview.com Ⓒ Ⓢ

Whether your bedroom is bedecked in gingham or outfitted in stainless steel, Widerview Village has you covered. The site opens into three different boutiques, each with furnishings to suit a specific taste: rustic, natural, or urban. There are also links for garden accoutrements, kitchenware, and gifts.

CosmopolitanHome.com www.cosmopolitanhome.com

Gorgeous candles, mirrors, draperies, and swank furniture at eyebrow-raising prices (an armoire for $2,192) can be found at CosmopoitanHome.com. This Philadelphia-based store is notable for cool merchandise, free delivery, and in-home setup.

Williams-Sonoma www.williams-sonoma.com (d) (s)
What started as a small neighborhood French cookware shop is now, well, Williams-Sonoma—the chain and catalog of upscale kitchenware and gifts. Shop their online store for top-quality cutlery, appliances, glassware, cookbooks, and furniture. The beautiful site provides some thoughtful touches to make shopping easier. For one thing, you can specify whether items should be shipped to you or to someone else as you build your shopping cart, saving you from having to complete two separate orders when purchasing gifts.

RabidHome.com www.rabidhome.com (d) (s)
RabidHome.com offers Asian-influenced wares for your home, bath, and desk. Pick up an herbal remedy kit, a ruby-colored angora pillow, or a set of wooden teacups—the common theme throughout the diverse stock is impeccable design and relatively moderate pricing. Free shipping, free wrapping, and live chat help are available.

Smith & Hawken www.smithandhawken.com
If most of your friends are of the fine and feathered type, Smith & Hawken's amazing bird feeders will have them flocking. (A corncob windmill! A millet wishing well!) Of course, if you're more nature lover than nature, the site also has beautiful home accessories, quality garden supplies, and clothes that will make you want to get out and weed. While you're shopping, be sure to stop by the resources link for great how-tos on topics like cooking from your garden and forcing bulbs.

Garden.com www.garden.com (c) (s)
Whether you have an urban window box or a full-scale rose garden, Garden.com has products and solutions for you. The site offers a full selection of seeds and bulbs (shipped overnight), plus accessories, gardening tips, and a community of other gardeners with whom you can share strategies. The extensive Design a Garden feature takes your existing light and climate considerations into account to help you choose flowers and plants to suit any patch of green.

Buildscape www.buildscape.com (c) (s)
Another everything-plus-the-kitchen-sink hardware superstore. Buildscape offers how-to advice, news and articles, auctions, remodeling plans, and ways to finance your home and find a reliable contractor. Whatever happened to just selling products?

HomeTownStores.com www.hometownstores.com (c) (d) (s)
Whether you're going to a barn-raising or just trying to fix the kitchen sink, HomeTownStores.com can probably set you up with the tools you need. The service really can't be beat here—everything from the live online help feature to the "no questions asked" return policy indicates that this operation wants to attract and keep your business. Shop for appliances, hand tools, paint, fasteners, and more.

YardMart.com www.yardmart.com ⓒ
From planting to pruning to patio partying, this site has nearly every outdoor need covered. Check out the selection of lawnmowers, clippers, and assorted tools to whip your weed patch into shape. Once you're finished, buy a barbecue, choose any of a dozen hammocks, grab a mint julep, and invite over the neighbors. What to do if you've picked the wrong shears? Call within ten days of receiving the item to get an authorization code for credit upon return.

GardenSolutions www.gardensolutions.com ⓒ ⓢ
If you can't find a product or helpful botanical hint at GardenSolutions, you probably don't have your eyes open. Not only does this site have all the shrubs, trees, and flowers you could ever want, it's also got answers to more than 17,000 questions on—what else?—gardening. Check out the Flower Finder for a list of all the plants that can thrive in your environment; ideal if you're trying to grow orchids at your Maine summer house.

Internet Malls

Yahoo! Shopping shopping.yahoo.com
Use Yahoo! Shopping to search for products across thousands of Yahoo!-affiliated stores, including macys.com, FTD, and Eddie Bauer, among numerous other homegrown outfits. Yahoo! just keeps on inventing features to make our lives easier (as if shopping here weren't convenient enough); sign up for the free Yahoo! Wallet, for example, and the site stores all your credit card and shipping information in one secure place.

SHOPPING.com www.shopping.com
As overwhelming as waking up in a mall in the middle of the night, SHOPPING.com offers too many options all at once. The focus here is on name brand computers, electronics, music, and videos (this is not the place to do your fashion shopping). One nice thing is the 125% guarantee; if you aren't satisfied with your purchase, SHOPPING.com will give you a gift certificate for more than the price you paid—but only after you fill out a grueling questionnaire.

coolshopping.com www.coolshopping.com ⓓ
If finding cool shopping sites seems like searching for a needle in a haystack, consider coolshopping.com your metal detector. This site handpicks the best shopping sites across the board and breaks them into categories for easy browsing. Check out the Recent Additions to see what they've just added, or hit the Site of the Day link for a random gem. The reviewers' taste may not always match yours, but skim the reviewer bios anyway—you might find a kindred soul.

ClickRewards www.clickrewards.com
Think frequent-flyer miles for online shopping and you've got the idea behind ClickRewards. Simply shop at participating stores (a list that includes heavies like eve.com, OfficeMax.com, Cooking.com, and eBags) to accumulate ClickMiles, then redeem them for toys, electronics, hotel discounts, and books. If you're really into the frequent-flyer idea, use your miles at any of the eight major airlines that accept them. Just think: a free digital camera is only 30,000 ClickMiles away.

iMALL www.imall.com
IMALL can take you to those little sites along the Web that tend to get overshadowed by the giants. The payoff is doing business with small merchants who can afford to give you the care and attention you love. What's lost are the big, quality sites with hard-to-find items the little guys may not carry. Great for dedicated surfers who want to get the full scope of what's out there.

eShop www.eshop.com
Lunch hour cyber-shoppers: save valuable seconds by bookmarking eShop. This e-commerce portal presents a buffet of links to big-name stores (like gap.com and wine.com) for quick and easy shopping. Buying for someone else? Go to the gift guides to get worthwhile, if somewhat predictable, suggestions. Or check out the daily and weekly specials to see a convenient list of money-savers gathered together for you.

Jewelry

Mondera.com www.mondera.com
There's truly something for everyone at Mondera.com, whether your style is elegant, casual, traditional, modern, or exotic. The site that claimed to have brokered the largest online diamond sale ever—a cool $96,000 for two loose stones—can hook you up with estate jewelry, an antique bracelet, or a wedding band.

NetJewels.com www.netjewels.com
An Internet-only jewelry retailer, NetJewels.com allows customers to research, price, and purchase a bauble, and to have it delivered to their door within 24 hours. If you can't find something you like in their extensive catalog, you can always custom design a piece to meet your specifications. With nearly 20 stones and eight metals to choose from, you're sure to find something to your liking.

netjewels.com

Blue Nile www.bluenile.com ©
No idea where to begin shopping for that engagement ring? Start with Blue Nile's exhaustive Diamond and Ring Guides, which explain ring-related terms like clarity, brilliance, and fire. Then browse through over 20,000 diamond rings and loose stones, all of which have been subjected to independent lab tests. Should you decide to buy, you'll have thirty days to evaluate your new rock and decide whether you'd like to return it for a refund (minus shipping costs).

Miadora
www.miadora.com (c)

Unsure what to get her for your anniversary? Want to propose to him but haven't found the right ring? Try Miadora. This online jeweler has hundreds of rings, bracelets, earrings, and pendants, including an impressive men's collection. You can search by type of metal, stone, designer, or price range, or browse the pre-owned estate jewelry. There's even a section that will give you suggestions for your brother, grandmother, or friend, searchable by occasion.

Zales Jewelers www.zales.com
Zales began as a little store in Texas dedicated to selling fine diamonds to average Americans through $1.00–a–week payment plans. And while the price of precious stones has gone up considerably since 1924, customers can still find terrific bargains on everything from aquamarine flower bracelets to Yves St. Laurent sport watches. You can also buy certified diamonds here.

tiffany.com www.tiffany.com (d)
Audrey Hepburn might have been amused to discover that she could window shop at Tiffany during breakfast without even going outside. The Web site of this jewelry store-cum-cultural icon is home to fine jewelry, china, and silver, plus sections on diamond buying and jewelry care. Returns can be made for 30 days, by mail or to a Tiffany store.

GoldandDiamond.com www.goldanddiamond.com
Order today, go out sparkling tomorrow night; GoldandDiamond.com's jewelry search engine lets you search by price (from under $300 to over $5,000) to find something beautiful and affordable for any occasion. You can narrow down your choices by stone, metal, and jewelry type. If you fall in love with a more expensive item, put it on layaway. The styles run traditional, but a huge variety of charms, brooches, watches, and pendants is also offered.

Claire's Accessories www.claires.com (d)
A haven for pop culture-savvy teens, Claire's Accessories offers jewelry, cosmetics, furniture, and fashion for the under-18 set. Read the fashion news, skim the hot trends ("thumb rings are the 'IN' ring this fall"), or learn how to create a new hairstyle. One of the neatest features is Claire's Room, which allows you to place furniture and decorations wherever you want them in any one of three virtual rooms. You'll know where everything you've ordered will go before it even arrives at your house!

SilverSpot.com www.silverspot.com
Quick, no-frills shopping for silver bracelets, earrings, and the like. The selection at SilverSpot.com is somewhat limited, but with free priority shipping within the U.S. and a free cleaning cloth with every jewelry order, this site is the place to go to scratch that silver itch.

Movies & Videos

bigstar.com www.bigstar.com (c)
Will Quentin Tarantino ever get over the '70s? What has Paul "Pee-Wee Herman" Reubens been doing with his free time? For celebrity-obsessed fans, there's only one place to buy videos and DVDs: bigstar.com. In addition to the requisite comedies, dramas, and new releases, this site features a large archive of celebrity interviews to answer all your burning questions. Sign up for video alert and the site will automatically send you an e-mail message when a long-anticipated movie is released on video or DVD.

Blockbuster.com www.blockbuster.com (s)
With nary an NC-17 video in sight, concerned citizens can feel secure in the knowledge that only movies with good old American values are available at Blockbuster.com. That's right, folks: *Rambo*, *Terminator*, and *Deathwish* are all ready to be shipped to your home in record time, so have your credit card ready. You'll also find video games, movie soundtracks, and a handy store locator at this site. Count on Blockbuster to be there 24 hours a day, seven days a week to help you out if anything goes amiss.

BlackStar.co.uk www.blackstar.co.uk (s)
Personalized service is the hallmark of BlackStar.co.uk, a British operation that claims to have helped customers with personal problems, career difficulties, and math equations, in addition to selling them videos. Yes, you will find videos and DVDs here, as well as a useful Video Hunt service which tracks down rare and out-of-print tapes. Nearly all the videos at BlackStar.co.uk are in PAL format, which means that only European VCRs can play them.

DVD Wave www.dvdwave.com (d) (s)
Free shipping, no sales tax ... and DVD Wave has great buys on DVD players, stereos, TV/VCR combos, Sony PlayStations, and Nintendo Game Boys. Oh yeah, and did we mention that they carry DVDs as well? If you find the same movie for less elsewhere, DVD Wave will refund the difference to your credit card.

DVD EXPRESS
www.dvdexpress.com
Ⓒ Ⓢ

The key to this store's success is volume, volume, volume. Virtually every conceivable DVD on the market is available here, and consequently the prices are often unbeatable. If the new titles are still too rich for your blood, dip down into the Bargain Basement, where we found major motion pictures like *Sense and Sensibility* and *Apocalypse Now* for 50% off.

eMerchandise www.emerchandise.com Ⓢ

Search by movie or TV show to find tons of cool entertainment-related gear, like *Star Wars* film cells and Wallace and Gromit T-shirts; the site also carries collectible comic, cartoon, and japanimation merchandise. You'll be amazed at the things you can find, like film scripts, playing cards, jewelry, mouse pads, puppets, and zipper pulls. If you're into it, sign up for eMerchandise's truly entertaining e-newsletter, which describes specials and upcoming releases.

DVD Planet www.dvdplanet.com

And they said DVDs would never catch on. DVD Planet (formerly Ken Crane's) gets kudos for excellent prices and a solid selection of laserdiscs and DTS titles (in addition to DVDs). You can browse top 10 lists or skim the new releases for ideas on what to buy. Be aware that if you receive merchandise that's defective, you'll have 14 days to exchange it for the same title only; luckily, DVD Planet will foot the bill for shipping.

Reel.com www.reel.com Ⓒ

Backing its gigantic store of merchandise with thoughtful reviews and entertaining articles, Reel.com is geared to people who like "movies," not "films." Though you won't find many obscure titles, the video superstore is an awesome place to find the old (and new) favorites you and your family can't live without. The news features here are well-written and discerning, preferring to report stories of merit (e.g., the Venice Film Festival) to tales gone stale (like Sharon Stone's latest temper tantrum).

NetFlix.com www.netflix.com

Still trying to set the clock on your VCR? Why not just throw the damn thing out and get a DVD player? With over 4,700 titles in stock, NetFlix.com offers some of the best deals on DVD rentals anywhere. It's unbelievably easy: Netflix.com sends the movie to your door, you send it back in a prepaid mailer within seven days. You'd be hard pressed to find another place that offers extended rentals for a mere 99 cents each week. Marquee members can enjoy four free movies per month and no late fees for the small price of a membership. No, that's not a misprint!

shopPBS shop.pbs.org

Nothing but quality programming here. You'll find everything from hilarious British comedy to nature programs and classic PBS documentaries, all relatively inexpensive and available to order online. Pump up your IQ (try Ken Burns' *The Civil War*) or your bod (with a *Fit or Fat* work-out tape)–you'll be supporting public television while you're at it.

Music

CheckOut.com www.checkout.com

Sometimes you just want the music, without the frills. CheckOut.com has all of the CDs, movies, and DVDs you're used to finding at a mall store, plus games, editor's reviews, the Billboard Top 20, and free digital downloads you'll only get online. Go to the SpeakOut section for chat and other diversions aimed at a youngish crowd. The layout is a bit overwhelming, so budget a few minutes to sort through it.

SecondSpin.com www.secondspin.com

CDs, videos, and DVDs may not improve with age, but their prices certainly do. SecondSpin.com, the self-proclaimed "Largest Buyer and Seller" of used music and videos in the world, has so much cheap stock, the boast just might fit. Surf here for great deals on obscure oldies, as well as picks so recently released, you won't believe they're used. To get the goods that go fast, browse the Just In Bin, which is full of items added in the last 24 hours. The site's a slow loader but, if time is money, it's worth the wait.

musicmaker.com www.musicmaker.com

Scrap your old mix tapes and head for musicmaker.com. A veritable mecca for music lovers, this site lets you choose all the songs for your own, personal compilation CD—up to 20 tracks or 70 minutes of play time. Listen to samples, choose the tracks you like, put them in sequence, and then click to order. Musicmaker.com will also suggest artists and songs that you might like, based on past selections. While not always accurate, the feature has potential.

Insound www.insound.com

Ambient, post-punk, lo-fi: if you know what these words mean, this site is for you. Insound is dedicated to the genres of music that get shafted at most of the larger online music retailers. Point your browser here for music chat, MP3s, a photo gallery, and, of course, CD shopping. And don't miss the Annex, a page devoted to LPs, 10-inches, 7-inches, music 'zines, and other hard-to-find stuff. Domestic shipping is free if you buy two or more items.

towerrecords.com www.towerrecords.com ⓒ

The best part of Tower Records' brick-and-mortar stores is also the best part of its Web site: the listening stations. Listen to excerpts from all the tracks on more than 80 albums without waiting in line. Additional online services include pre-ordering for new releases, an easy-to-search Out of Print section, and a solid selection of CDs under $7. The customer service information isn't prominent, but you will find a phone number and e-mail address if you dig for it.

Columbia House www.columbiahouse.com

As if the lure of 12 free CDs wasn't enticing enough by mail, the Columbia House Web site makes it even easier to join up and cash in. Use the search engine to find the dozen albums you want—no more poring over the mailers with the stamps and the five-point font. You're obligated to buy just five more selections at regular prices. The best part? No more automatic shipments. The selection is eminently predictable; surf here for mainstream favorites only.

Collectors' Choice Music www.ccmusic.com

The best shop for music aficionados to feed their aural fixation. Collector's Choice Music probably has the rare CD you seek, be it the Narada Nutcracker or the new Nine Inch Nails import. The site's intense search engine lets you search for music by genre (Big Band, Folk, '60s Rock), artist, album, song, and even label. If you don't have anything specific in mind, look to the Top 100 or browse the Close Outs for eclectic discs at half price.

GEMM www.gemm.com
Most people spend three months comparison shopping for a car but don't spend three minutes looking for better music prices. GEMM compiles the inventory of hundreds of different small record stores into a searchable database, making it easy to find a discount price for almost any new or used CD, LP, or cassette. (Search for videos and books here too.) There's very little information available on individual albums beyond title and label, but if you know what you want, GEMM will help you find a deal.

zZounds www.zzounds.com
ZZounds is made for the band geek in each of us. Every instrument and instrument accessory under the sun is in stock here, from amplifiers to zithers. You can also learn more about your instrument in the Featured Content section, or shop for printed music. Though the home page is geared toward guitarists, a quick search will unearth anything your little musical heart desires.

The CD Exchange www.thecdexchange.com
Admit it. We've all got records we're ashamed to own, whether it's RATT's first album or the orchestral version of "Ice, Ice Baby." Now's the time to capitalize on your former lack of taste. Stop in to The CD Exchange and sell your old stuff for cold, hard cash; you send the site an e-mail with your "for sale" titles and they'll respond with a price. You can also browse the catalog of available used CDs and, if you're in the mood to haggle, propose a trade. The prices are unbeatable, but the site suffers for lack of a search engine.

Jump! Music www.jumpmusic.com ⓒ
For anyone who noodles around on the guitar (or any other instrument) and wants a little more direction, Jump! Music sells sheet music to all your favorite songs. It doesn't matter whether you're an oboe-playing rock fan or a pianist with a taste for gospel; you'll find something you like here. Added perk: Real Audio samples of nearly every song on paper.

Case Logic www.caselogic.com
After you've filled up your shopping cart at all your favorite online CD stores, head for Case Logic and buy a place to store them all. Their expanded online catalog has the company's popular CD wallets and storage cases, as well as camera bags, car organizers, and laptop bags. While Case Logic's customer service policies and warranties are generous by most standards, the site would benefit from a privacy policy that states clearly what the company does with personal information registered on the site.

ARTISTdirect www.artistdirect.com
Where can you find the very latest music and fan gear? ARTISTdirect. The site links to individual artists' own e-stores. Buy the Beastie Boys' new release right off their home page, tune in for a Cher Webcast, or shop at the ARTISTdirect Superstore, which has CDs, merchandise, and apparel from lesser-knowns.

Listen.com www.listen.com (c)

Downloading MP3s from random Web sites could get you a nasty visit from the Secret Music Police. That's where Listen.com comes in. This site is a huge index of legally downloadable music, both free and for sale. Picks include the usual pop hits, plus soul, spoken word, and even show tunes. The site's outstanding beginner and advanced guides will hold your hand through the entire process of getting a player and downloading files.

AudioWeb www.audioweb.com (c)

When audiophiles venture out of their natural habitat (buried in an armchair near the business end of a premium system), they congregate at AudioWeb. The site began in 1994 as a collection of classifieds, but has since grown to include audio equipment, product reviews, auctions, discussion groups, and an audio newsstand. The stock is geared toward design-minded connoisseurs; you'll find names like Granite Audio and Laser Base rather than Sony and Panasonic.

CoolAudio.com www.coolaudio.com (s)

For those of us who can't afford to drop $1,000 on a CD player, there's CoolAudio.com. With audio and video equipment for every price range (the CD players here range from $165 to $7,100), a home theater system is finally within your means. Use the personal recommendation feature to narrow down your choices or the glossary to decode hi-fi terms. At CoolAudio.com, the more you spend, the better the perks: purchases over $1,500 qualify you for free set-up and installation and free pick-up on returns.

Bose www.bose.com (d)

Bose is the Rolls Royce of audio equipment, selling top-of-the-line speakers for home systems and automobiles. The company's long list of satisfied customers includes Madison Square Garden and the Sistine Chapel; you too can have stadium-quality sound in your home if you're willing to pay for it. Especially cool items include the Lifestyles line of home audio, which features tiny four-and-a-half inch speakers (you could hold four of them in your palm), and the Acoustic Wave series that lets you take Bose quality to go.

CDNOW www.cdnow.com (c) (s)

What do you get when you cross Sheryl Crow, INXS, and Brahms? CDNOW's Album Advisor takes three of your favorite artists and suggests other music you might enjoy, making it easy to discover new music. The site's focus on personalized content simply blows the competition out of the water; after browsing CDNOW's sizable assortment of reviews, audio clips, and CDs, click on My CDNOW for a personalized start page that includes your order history, wish list, and recommendations tailored to your musical tastes. (By the way, the answer is Jimi Hendrix.)

CDNOW

cdnow.com

RioPort.com www.rioport.com Ⓒ

In case you haven't heard, the Rio Player is a cool, portable music device that lets you listen to digital music files (like MP3s) on the go. At RioPort.com, buy a player, then download as many (legal) MP3s as you want. There's plenty of music here, and the site also has short stories, educational clips, and spoken word pieces. (Including a sound file of Winston Churchill reading his own autobiography.) Nearly all the files are free, but a few cost up to $2.00. Need help? Click on Dr. Download for a thorough FAQ, but don't expect further customer service.

Office Products

OfficeDepot.com www.officedepot.com Ⓒ Ⓢ

Office Depot's awesome online store offers way more than just staplers and file folders. The site is loaded with extras like their office toolkit (complete with downloadable contracts, forms, and business letters) and tips on how to get organized, set up a home office, and even start a company Web site. To get the most out of the site, set up an account and take advantage of customized shopping lists.

Staples.com www.staples.com Ⓒ

Buying office products can be quite a chore—marching up and down warehouse aisles, finding the right printer cartridge, choosing fine-tip or extra fine-tip pens. For simpler shopping, head to Staples.com, the comprehensive source for pins, pens, file folders, furniture, and everything else. Become a registered shopper (free!) and the site adapts to you by keeping track of your purchase history and favorite "aisles," or product genres. The more you shop, the better the site knows you and the faster you can get back to work.

works.com
business purchasing online

Works.com
www.works.com
When you need a wrist rest pronto, the last thing you want is to get caught in office bureaucracy. Works.com brings office supply purchasing online: an employee enters a request (for correction fluid or a paper shredder or coffee cups), Works.com sends an e-mail to the correct person for approval, and the order is sent on to the warehouse. The supplies are shipped by UPS, at no charge for orders of more than $25. With the money and time you can save on more than 20,000 products, isn't it worth seeing if the site will work for your business?

Atypical-Cube www.atypical-cube.com
You spend a quarter of your life at the office (if you work full time), so why not spice up your space? Atypical-Cube has desktop fountains, silk storage boxes, quirky lamps, and miniature Zen gardens you won't find anywhere else, all returnable within 30 days. Satisfaction—and co-worker envy—guaranteed.

FranklinCovey.com www.franklincovey.com
New Year's resolution, milestone birthday, or pure frustration: there are plenty of reasons to start organizing your life, and FranklinCovey.com has the tools to do it. Customize a day planner with their daily and monthly pages, expense sheets, check registers, shopping lists, and more, or pick up refills if you're already a convert. If all else fails, a weekend workshop with the Franklin Covey pros should set you straight.

the home office store www.thehomeofficestore.com
It's time to end your office romance—with the color beige. The home office store has smart, well-designed desk accessories in meadow green, cayenne red, and other sizzling colors that beat the pants off old vanilla manila. Filing may not be exciting, but your file folders can be.

Levenger www.levenger.com
You will have to shell out some serious cash to shop here, but Levenger's merchandise—marketed toward "professional readers, writers, and communicators"—is impressive indeed, and includes everything from top-quality furniture to fountain pens and desk accessories. The site isn't much more than a catalog translated to the Web, but we can withstand the clunky interface for top-quality products like these.

Shop121.com www.shop121.com
Shop121.com isn't fancy, but it is well organized. The site sells all manner of office furniture, from computer desks to chairs and file cabinets. Deck out your whole office with one of their "collections" or shop by product category. Once you choose a category, you'll see a dizzying array of options to help you narrow your search (more than 15 options for chair backs alone). If you're not that picky, just check "no preference" to view the whole selection.

inkfarm.com www.inkfarm.com
Nothing puts dread in the heart of an office bee like the creeping signs of printer cartridge death. Thankfully, inkfarm.com's streamlined site will get you a new cartridge in five clicks flat–simply choose brand, model, quantity, check out, and shipping method. With a 90-day return policy, no restocking fees, and free shipping, there's no better way to keep the office in ink.

iPrint.com www.iprint.com (d)
Don't point your browser here unless you have 30 minutes to spare–the site's products and interface are tough to resist. IPrint.com is a fully interactive online design shop that lets you personalize everything from greeting cards to wall clocks and address labels. Their step-by-step guidelines can take you from choosing card stock to arranging text and graphics to entering a print order. Need business cards? This is the place for professional-looking results at a price that won't break the bank.

StampsOnline www.stampsonline.com
Say you break a leg and have a lot of time to write letters. Thanks to StampsOnline, you won't have to go to the post office for stamps. This U.S. Postal Service site will sell you hundreds of different kinds of stamps, including collectibles and holiday-themed postage. There's even a useful list of philatelic societies across the U.S. for collectors.

Stamps.com www.stamps.com
It may be one of the best kept Internet secrets that you can actually buy and print U.S. Mail postage at home. Go to Stamps.com, which is officially approved by the U.S. Postal Service, to download the free software you'll need. The site requires you to pay a small fee (just as you would for a postage meter), but once you've set it up, you can print postage as often as you need. You can also pick up more traditional mailing supplies here, including labels, envelopes, and scales.

eFax.com www.efax.com
Don't have a fax machine at home? Head for eFax.com, the originator of the fax/e-mail interface. Not sure how it works? Here are the fax: Sign up at the company's Web site to receive a fax number. When friends or colleagues send you a fax, the fax is transformed into an image and sent to your e-mail address, where you can view it as an attachment. Oh, did we mention that the service is advertiser-supported and entirely free to you?

Pet Supplies

Pets.com www.pets.com (c) (d)
A simple way to buy supplies, food, toys, and gifts for anything with fur, feathers, or fins. You'll find the usual selection of pet products here, as well as some unique items, like ferret hammocks, gourmet doggie treats, and freeze-dried fish food. All kinds of resident experts are on call at Pets.com to answer burning questions on products (What is a Booda Velvet?), pet health (cures for persistent vomiting), and even animal law.

Petstore.com www.petstore.com (c) (d) (s)
If you've ever shaken your fist at an empty 20-pound bag of dog food and shouted, "As God is my witness, Rover will never be hungry again," back up your promise with a trip to Petstore.com. Not only will they deliver supplies at regular intervals to your home, they also offer free shipping on all orders less than 50 pounds, on-call animal experts, and Solution Kits to take care of hairballs, shedding, and "accidents."

Petopia.com www.petopia.com (c) (d) (s)

Petopia.com™
The Internet Pet Paradise™

This cunning little site offers all the pet-supply standbys, plus specialized merchandise like peanut butter-flavored dog cookies and climb-n-sail ferret boats. Be sure to drop in on one of Petopia.com's many discussion forums; whether you own saltwater fish or barnyard animals, you're bound to find a kindred spirit here.

J-B Wholesale Pet Supplies www.jbpet.com
This site is ideal for people who have a financial investment in their pets, as it's one of the few places to carry grooming supplies worthy of show animals. The staff consists of folks who have years of experience showing, breeding, and training animals. Plus, J-B Wholesale Pet Supplies deals directly with pet supply manufacturers, passing the savings on to lucky you.

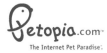

In The Company of Dogs
www.inthecompanyofdogs.com
If your dog has an extensive wardrobe of velvet T-shirts, faux fur jackets, and tailgate jerseys, it can afford to pass by this Web site. If not, you owe it to your precious pooch to drop by and stock up on essentials. While you're here, browse the selection of artwork, garden statues, pillows, and bath mats emblazoned with (surprise!) dogs. Must be seen to be believed.

Price Comparisons

bottomdollar.com www.bottomdollar.com

bottomdollar.com™

If you're squeezing your pennies till they hurt, this is your kind of place. Enter the item you want and bottomdollar.com will search online stores to find you the cheapest prices. A nice touch–instead of just listing the cheapest, it lets you choose from a long list, so you can be as picky and specific as you want. Warning: you may get overwhelmed by your savings–there are about thirty cheapie listings for Tylenol alone.

E-Compare www.ecompare.com

Save your wrist some work and let E-compare do the surfing. This site searches big name stores for the product you seek and gives back a list of where to get the lowest prices. For example, enter "toaster," and E-Compare browses for bargains at Digital Chef, Cooking.com, and KitchenEmporium. Because it searches only a limited number of sites, you may have trouble finding more unusual things, but if your item is a common one, this is an easy way to comparison shop.

Jango www.jango.com

Excite's product finder is simple and user-friendly, making it easy to locate information and prices on everything from power tools to Portland Roses. Simply enter the specific item you want (Portland Rose) or a general category (flowers – live plants), and hit either "Find Reviews" or "Find Prices." The site returns an info-packed buyers guide, or a list of links that allow you to purchase your roses from whichever merchant you choose. It's e-commerce at its simplest.

DealPilot.com www.dealpilot.com

Like GEMM, DealPilot.com compares prices on books, movies, and music. Unlike GEMM, it focuses primarily on major Internet stores. Pros: you'll be dealing largely with companies you've heard of before. Cons: DealPilot.com has a somewhat more limited selection than GEMM, and its prices are nowhere near as competitive. You can also download DealPilotExpress, a program that surfs along with you and automatically compares prices on whatever item you've found while shopping.

mySimon www.mysimon.com ⓒ

Meet your own personal shopper–even if he does have a maniacal expression on his face. MySimon is one of the best price comparison services around, searching over 2,000 merchants for the best prices on everything from a surfboard to a new hard drive. You'll also find daily shopping news, consumer resources, and detailed information on each merchant. Before you buy, be sure to check in with Simon first.

PriceSCAN.com www.pricescan.com
PriceSCAN.com will find you fabulous prices on the stuff you love, regardless if a merchant offering a bargain has a Web site or not. Best of all, PriceSCAN.com doesn't accept money from vendors, so the search results are unbiased and amazingly thorough. The interface could be snazzier, but this is an otherwise good source for bargain hunting.

DealTime.com www.dealtime.com
A Web site that calls you when it finds the price you want on a new digital camera? Believe it. Enter the price you want to pay for any item, and DealTime.com will notify you by e-mail or phone when the product goes on sale. The site also provides links to product information and reviews. Not sure what you want to buy? Check out the QuickShop link for the deal of the day.

Sale Finders

inshop.com www.inshop.com ⓒ ⓓ
It's like hiring your own personal shopper, but better: 24 hours a day, 7 days a week, Inshop.com is on call to keep you posted on the sales at all your favorite stores and spas, from Barney's to Bloomies. Loads of great deals await—just select a city and the product, designer, or store you want (everything from furniture to Frederic Fekkai is here); InShop gives you the lowdown on where and when to buy at discounts of up to 50%.

StyleShop.com www.styleshop.com ⓒ
When in Rome, shop as the Romans do: StyleShop.com's got city guides that tell you what's on sale in over 200 cities across the country. Sample sales, store guides, and dozens of great deals await—just select the city, click the date, and find out what sales are on at Barney's, Armani, and Dolce & Gabbana, among others. The site even provides directions to your desired shopping destination!

SALEseeker www.saleseeker.com
Use SALEseeker to scour stores, Web sites, and catalogs for terrific buys on everything from clothes to furniture to automotive supplies. As you might expect, the results are hit-or-miss, depending on the season and your area. The impressive list of retailers includes Sears, OfficeMax and Pier 1 Imports, but this small sample hardly does the content justice. Definitely worth a peek.

Search Engines

Buyer's Index www.buyersindex.com ⓒ
With more than 96 million products listed in its database, Buyer's Index can almost certainly find what you're looking for, be it Elvis memorabilia or a silk bathrobe. This is one of the most accurate shopping search engines we've found. Items are sorted by product, category, and brand; the more specific the keywords you enter, the better your search results will be.

GTE superpages.com www.superpages.com ⓒ
Find a doctor, dentist, mechanic, florist, or (gulp) funeral home in a time of need. GTE superpages.com is a complete online version of the Yellow Pages, with search features that make it easy to find specific products, driving directions, or business phone numbers and addresses. Check out the city guides for shopping information that's customized to your locale. If you're hosting a party, buying a car, or starting a business, the Idea pages will point you in the right direction.

The All-Internet Shopping Directory www.all-internet.com
The All-Internet Shopping Directory is a no-frills search interface that scans thousands of e-merchants for the products you seek. Keep in mind that All-Internet simply provides listings of stores; you'll have to check for yourself whether the sites offer secure purchasing and other essentials. Since there's no particular ranking here, you'll have quite a bit of sifting to do, but thorough shoppers may enjoy slogging through the mire to get to that rare gold nugget.

Brandpoint www.brandpoint.com
Brandpoint is, to put it simply, a list of links to 500 of the best brand-name online shops (and informational sites), sorted by genre. No need to sort through stores you've never heard of when you can go straight to trusted names like Best Buy, Bloomingdale's, and Barbie. After shopping on other sites, you'll find the pared-down interface here a refreshing change as well.

Shoes

NORDSTROMshoes.com shoes.nordstrom.com (c) (d) (s)
Nordstrom's online shoe store deserves raves for its gorgeous selection (brands like BCBG, Kenneth Cole, and Via Spiga), and for its commitment to finding the perfect fit for your feet. First, take the site's Shoe Quiz, which can help you determine your size. If you haven't been measured at a store in the last year, you can use the site's printable sizing device (just like the silver ones you see in shoe stores, only on paper) to measure your feet at home. It's easy!

onlineshoes.com www.onlineshoes.com (s)
Ecco, Rockport, Vans, and Wigwam all live at onlineshoes.com, where selection and style reign supreme. There are some gaps in the inventory here: the dress shoes aren't snazzy enough for formal occasions, and there isn't any footwear for kids. Anyone seeking casual chic will feel right at home, though, and the site spells out customer service information in clear, easy-to-understand language. If the shoes don't fit, return them within 30 days for a full refund.

Nine West www.ninewest.com (d) (s)
If you're a woman (or a freaky kind of guy), chances are you've got a pair of Nine West sandals, moccasins, or maryjanes in your closet. The prices at this online store are super-reasonable, considering the quality; for $70 dollars or less you can buy beaded sandals, cool clogs, or classic loafers here. Register at Club Nine to get express ordering, a personal address book for sending gifts, and periodic e-mail updates (if you so desire).

Payless.com www.payless.com (s)
Don't let the name fool you: these shoes may be cheap, but they hardly look it. Sure, some models may give you a blister or two, but when you need a pair of glittery platform sandals that are priced to move, this is the place to go. In addition to dazzling dress shoes, Payless.com also has comfort and athletic footwear for tooling around town. Go to the Shoe Finder to search Payless' stock by size; if you have a particular shoe that you buy regularly, the Lot Finder link will take you straight to it.

Zappos.com www.zappos.com (d)
Offering more than 100 brands of shoes in every conceivable style, Zappos.com is a boon for footwear fans. High-profile labels include Enzo, L.B. Evans, Rockport, and EasySpirit; there's a respectable selection of kids' styles as well. Shopping here is truly a calming experience; the site lets you breeze through the different sections with minimal clicks, and offers just enough information for you to know what you're buying.

SteveMadden.com www.stevemadden.com
Oooh ... knee-high platforms with four-inch heels ... red leather boots with silver buckles ... teetering pumps swathed in silver. The shoes will make you swoon. Even if you don't find anything to suit your taste, you simply must have a pair of Steve Madden's fuzzy bedroom slippers. Take your pick of lavender, pink, or baby blue.

Etienne Aigner www.etienneaigner.com
For classic, top-quality shoes, belts, and bags with a conservative feel, shop at Etienne Aigner. The company's no-frills site offers a limited selection of shoes (for women only), plus a comfort-oriented line called "easentials" with hard-to-find sizes. Check out the care instructions for a detailed primer on how to keep your leather items supple and polished, or the FAQ for a marginally helpful list of questions. Don't know how to pronounce the name? It's "Eh-tee-yen On-yay."

Florsheim www.florsheim.com
Come to Florsheim for beautiful dress, casual, and golf shoes for men; the shoes are fantastic, though the site itself could use some improvement. The navigation is clunky, the Casual Advice section is good for a laugh at best (let's hope nobody takes fashion this seriously, ever), and the lack of posted sales policies is no joking matter. Have a burning question that can only be answered by a podiatrist? Neither did we. (Though the site does offer the option to send e-mail to a member of the Podiatric Medical Association.)

Chinese Laundry Shoes www.chineselaundry.com ⓓ
Downtown looks for ladies. Go to Chinese Laundry Shoes for platforms, sandals, and chunky-heel boots in the latest styles. Their interactive site lets you view shoes in a variety of different colors—just scroll your mouse over the color swatches to see the shoe in every available hue.

nike.com www.nike.com ⓓ ⓢ
Nike deserves props for beefing up its site with stunning visuals, but with links labeled Flight, Force, and The Morning After, you may wonder whether you've stumbled on the site for *The Young and the Restless*. Don't panic, though; one click of the Store button will take you straight to the revered athletic shoes. The Product Finder at nike.com is better in theory than in practice; the site requires you to fill out an exhaustive questionnaire before giving recommendations, so you're probably better off searching by sport.

World Foot Locker Megastore www.footlocker.com (s)

Jocks who can go 10 rounds with Tyson but refuse to brave the crowds at Footlocker need not despair; they can now buy their favorite athletic shoes online. With more than 14,000 products and 150 brands, it's hard to conceive of a sneaker that isn't represented here—and endless inventory means terrific savings for you, sport-o. Need to return your shoe? Mail it in or take it to one of Footlocker's 2,500 stores.

shopreebok.com www.shopreebok.com

Download Macromedia Flash before you visit shopreebok.com; you'll need the plug-in to view this site at its best. You can browse a limited selection of footwear, clothing, and accessories here, or link to a dealer locator if the shoe you seek isn't offered. The technical specs are particularly helpful for folks with specific footgear needs; each product comes with a detailed description of its benefits and uses.

Finish Line www.finishline.com

A sneaker site with a community feel, Finish Line features a line of extra-wide footwear plus a warehouse full of athletic apparel for men, women, and children. Taking out a membership entitles you to free shipping on orders over $25, making this a great spot to shop for families. For fun, take a look at the Champions of Achievement section, which profiles promising young athletes from across the country.

Sneaker.com www.sneaker.com

Browse by sport for Nike, Adidas, Reebok, Puma, or Asics (among others), as well as shoes specially designed for tennis, golf, and soccer. The selection here isn't overwhelming, which makes for a manageable interface and easy surfing. You'll have 30 days to return merchandise, but be sure it's in the original packaging, else Sneaker.com may deny you a refund.

skechers.com www.skechers.com (s)

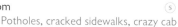

Potholes, cracked sidewalks, crazy cab drivers—to survive in the city these days, urban warriors need the right kind of shoes. Enter skechers.com, the store with cool-looking sneakers, casuals, and boots as indestructible as army tanks. The selection is comparable to what you might find in a department store—hip styles and a lot of lug soles—but much easier to search. Shop here and get a free T-shirt and free shipping to boot.

VANS www.vansshoes.com (d)

Forget skateboarding to the mall for a new pair of old skools. VANS makes it easy to buy shoes for skating, surfing, and shredding. Choose your gender and age group, pick one of the many kicky styles, and then flip through the color selections—you can view the shoes in all available colors, so you won't have to buy those Lime Retro Rectangle tennies on faith. Customer service won't bend over backwards for you, but you can mail back an unworn pair within 30 days of purchase.

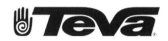

Airwalk www.airwalk.com
Visiting Airwalk's Web site may be like a baptism by fire for newcomers to the Internet. After oohing and aahing over the nifty graphics that pepper the splash page, head for the store and load up on shoes. Granted, the styles are aimed at skate and snowboarders (and your average teenager), but you're not too old to learn, are you, Gramps? After all, you took to the Net fast enough!

Teva Footwear www.teva.com
The inspiration for Tevas came to river guide Mark Thatcher back in 1982, when the soon-to-be-founder couldn't find a sandal suitable for navigating the Colorado River. The strappy shoe he invented may look delicate, but don't be fooled. Tevas can do battle with everything from cobblestones to hiking trails. The customer service page here is geared toward questions about the shoes rather than about the site; while we appreciate the information on cleaning and caring for Tevas, the site could stand some explanation of return policies and the like.

Keds www.keds.com
The classic comfort shoe. Choose styles for women, girls, and babies at truly affordable prices, or browse the casuals section for styles that could do in the workplace. Most Keds can even be thrown in the washing machine. The site's clean design makes it easy to navigate, but the only way to contact the customer service department is by sending an e-mail—we were hard-pressed to find a phone number anywhere on the site.

DesignerShoes.com www.designershoes.com
Amateurish presentation, but where else can you find a pair of strappy Via Spiga heels in size 11? Ladies with large feet will thrill at the prospect of decidedly non-frumpy shoes from names like Evan Picone, Bruno Magli, and Steve Madden in sizes nine through 14. A real find.

Oddball Shoe Company www.oddballshoe.com
Those size 14s need no longer be a source of shame, Bigfoot. That's because Oddball Shoe Company will discreetly ship men's coffin-sized Adidas, Clarks, Dr. Martens, and John Fluevogs right to your home. The cooler-than-thou design at this site (the Flash version is optional) will make you want to buy some shoes, even if you don't have large feet. And though customer service is closed on Sunday, according to the owners "you can still call 'cause we may be just hangin' out or cleaning the store or something."

adidas www.adidas.com
If you've got a hankering for baseball spikes, running shoes, or high tops from adidas, seek no further than the company's Web store, which has games, product promotions, downloads, and cool Flash animations in addition to the shoes. Like other brand sites, the adidas store is as much an extended commercial as it is a store. Still, if you've gotta have the shoes, browse the selection here or fill out a Wish List and e-mail it to a friend. Who says the Internet doesn't promote close relationships?

Sporting Goods

REI.com www.rei.com Ⓒ Ⓢ

The company that made it possible to look stylish while climbing a big hunk of granite has firmly established itself on the Net. After loading up on hiking, climbing, camping, cycling, and fishing gear at this massive store, be sure to pay a visit to the Learn and Share board, where you'll discover the best way to pack a backpack and the nicest places to hike around the world. There's even a gift registry here!

Tailgate Town www.tailgatetown.com

How loyal a fan are you? Sure you tailgate, but do your true colors shine through on flags, coolers, chairs, and cups? Both college and professional teams are represented at Tailgate Town, so be sure to stock up on supplies, lest the other guys out-spirit you. If the hats and jerseys don't draw you, the keg-shaped grill just might.

Road Runner Sports www.roadrunnersports.com Ⓒ

Road Runner Sports has over 150,000 running shoes available on its site (practically every brand with the notable exception of Nike), plus articles, race registration, an online auction, a runner's club, and products like heart monitors, insoles, water bottles, and nutritional supplements. This site is especially good for new runners seeking the encouragement to go the extra mile; we love the product reviews, injury information, and customized shoe search.

TSI Soccer www.tsisoccer.com

For anyone who plays soccer or simply must have a pair of striped calf socks, TSI's online store offers brand-name equipment like Mia Hamm T-shirts, Puma turf shoes, and Reebok warm-ups. The site is staffed by people who obviously love soccer, some of whom have played in the NCAA and the British Pub Leagues. What does that mean for you? Well-selected gear. Go to About Us for information on shipping, returns, and the like; there is no help page.

MVP.com www.mvp.com Ⓒ Ⓓ

Looking to buy a football but don't know your polyurethane from your polyvinyl chloride? Get the skinny on pigskin (and practically any other sporting equipment) directly from the pros who know: Elway, Jordan, and Gretzky. The powerhouse players have teamed up to bring you one of the most info-packed sporting goods sites online. Check out the buyer's guides here for expert advice on choosing equipment and protective gear; with advice from these guys, how could you possibly go wrong?

MountainZone.com www.mountainzone.com ⓒ

Start off on a new adventure or just look really cool at the ski lodge. MountainZone.com is primarily an informational site, but click on the Marketplace link and you'll find gear for hiking, climbing, and biking, in addition to comparison charts, buyer's guides, travel tips, and expedition tales. The National Parks Directory is worth surfing for stunning photos and tantalizing descriptions. The next best thing to being in the great outdoors.

Altrec.com www.altrec.com ⓒ ⓓ ⓢ

For the outdoor enthusiast who never goes inside, Altrec.com invites surfers to experience the great outdoors, plan for trips, and chat with fellow adventurers before choosing their gear. The articles and travel advisories here are intelligent and far better than most sports sites we've seen. Altrec.com will even help you accessorize and color-coordinate an ensemble with clothes, packs, and assorted gadgets in matching earth tones.

Patagonia www.patagonia.com ⓒ ⓢ

Browse by activity (backpacking, sailing, or ice climbing, for starters) to find jackets, pants, backpacks, outdoor accessories, and signature fleeces from Patagonia. All the gear here is top-quality and backed by a knowledgeable sales staff. The products are pricey ($155 for a fleece), but where else are you gonna go for a Gortex Ice-9 suit?

BigEdge.com www.bigedge.com ⓒ ⓓ ⓢ

Before shopping at BigEdge.com, link to Buyers Edge, the site's information section. The buyer's guides and product checklists here can help you choose the right gear for your sport—right down to the rim and the coaching whistle. There are also instructional videos on the site, though you'll have better chances of improving your shot if you turn off your computer and head for the gym.

Pro Webwear.com www.prowebwear.com

Wear your pride on your sleeve—literally—with a visit to Pro Webwear.com. Featuring hats, jerseys, and jackets emblazoned with the logos of college and professional teams, you'll finally be able to outfit yourself like those lunatics you see in sporting arenas all over the nation. For an extra-special treat, you can have your own name and your hero's number slapped on the NHL or NFL jersey of your choice.

NBA Store store.nba.com

Tired of shoddy knock-off team gear? Go straight to the NBA Store, which has authentic balls, jackets, and jerseys from respectable dealers like Champion, Nike, and Puma. While predictably expensive, this is the first place to stop when you get a hankering for some Utah Jazz shorts or an official WNBA Barbie. Sizing information for all the gear is available in the User Guide.

BackWoodsGrocery.com www.backwoodsgrocery.com

Firm evidence that camp food can be more than charred marshmallows and flaming frankfurters. Dial up this site to pick the dried fruit, dehydrated vegetables, freeze-dried meats, and canned potatoes you need to prepare a savory outdoor feast. There are also valuable tips on mastering outdoor cooking gear. (You never knew there were so many uses for tinfoil, did you?)

Sporting Auction www.sportingauction.com

What makes Sporting Auction cool enough to be included in this book? Well, for starters, free shipping. That's right: after you've secured a pair of rollerblades, a snowboard, or a sleeping bag, the site will ship the stuff right to your door at absolutely no additional cost to you. Everything sold here is brand new and brand name, so if you're looking for a bargain, be sure to take a peek.

Online Sports www.onlinesports.com

In addition to the basketball, soccer, and football gear you'd find at every other e-store, this site has equipment for sports you never knew existed, like broom hockey and corkball. Granted, the design isn't much to look at, but where else are you going to find a sparring body pad to practice your jeet kune do? Ideal for rugged individualists and eccentrics alike.

The Sports Store shop.sportsline.com

If you're rabid about your favorite sports team or a particular athlete, pay a visit to this Web site. It's got everything from athletic equipment to novelty items and gift baskets emblazoned with your team's logo or your hero's photograph. Search items by sport or just visit the specialty shops, which include such obscure stores as CricShop, NFL Europe, and WrestleLine. (Don't worry, cricket fans, you can pay in British pounds or American dollars.)

Eastern Mountain Sports www.shopems.com

Save your energy for the hike—get your supplies at Eastern Mountain Sports. The site has an enormous variety of equipment, apparel, and info for every outdoor adventure from bird watching to mountain biking. Activity-specific supply checklists provide foolproof preparedness for whatever outing you may be attempting; the site also provides detailed sizing information for clothes, hats, shoes, sleeping bags, and backpacks in the Fitting Area.

ShopSports.com www.shopsports.com (c)

An online sports superstore, this site has the fitness, outdoor, and athletic gear you love at prices that won't make you cramp up. All the big names are here, including Reebok, adidas, and Wilson, but the limited space allowed in this review can hardly do justice to the exhaustive content at ShopSports.com. If you're not suitably pumped after filling your shopping cart, check out the sports lounge, which has chat rooms, current scores, magazines, and fantasy games.

Justballs.com www.justballs.com (c)

In this world of superstores and warehouses, it's nice to find a place devoted to a single type of product. Justballs.com carries literally every type of ball, from medicine to pingpong to Nerf. Once you've got the balls, read the online encyclopedia and rules database, which provides rules and strategies for a variety of games.

The Backcountry Store www.backcountrystore.com (c) (s)

You might actually hear the call of the wild if you turned your modem off once in a while. But as long as you're on the Net anyway, pay a visit to The Backcountry Store. Its gigantic inventory of tents, sleeping bags, and cooking gear may tempt you back into the wilderness, and those handy maps and first-aid kits will enable you to make the return trip unscathed.

beOutdoors.com www.beoutdoors.com

You're sitting at the desk in your cubicle, alphabetizing the company's take-out menus and organizing your paper clips by size. It's time to visit beOutdoors.com and plan a weekend getaway. It's got everything you need to go boating, fishing, hunting, or camping, plus refresher courses on the dos and don'ts of outdoor sports. The customer service information here is almost too thorough; look up how to return a product and beOutdoors.com returns a 13-point checklist of information you must provide. Don't know about you, but we'd rather be fishing!

PlanetOutdoors.com www.planetoutdoors.com (d)

For athletes who would rather look good than feel good, there's PlanetOutdoors.com. While it's true you can shop by sport, the site is also eager to help customers choose items from the more than 100 designer labels here, including Swiss Army and The North Face. Hey, you never know who you'll run into on that mountain top!

Gear.com www.gear.com

Can't afford to join a gym? Well, that's no excuse to sit around the house: Gear.com has the equipment to keep you hale and hearty, all at close-out prices. More than 40 sports are represented here, including adventure travel, nordic skiing, and wakeboarding. Search by gender, price, or product. Gear.com will ship your purchase (no matter how large or small) for a mere 25 cents, so go ahead and stock up.

Fogdog Sports www.fogdog.com

Don't be misled by the URL; you won't find any chew toys here, just tons and tons of sporting equipment. Get all the gear and apparel for your favorite athletic activity here, from the majors (basketball, football, baseball, hockey) to the minors (lacrosse, gymnastics, wrestling). Browse the categories, sports, or concept shops, or just search by keyword. Who knows, you just might find something for Fido, too.

Capezio Dance Theatre Workshop www.capeziorvc.com

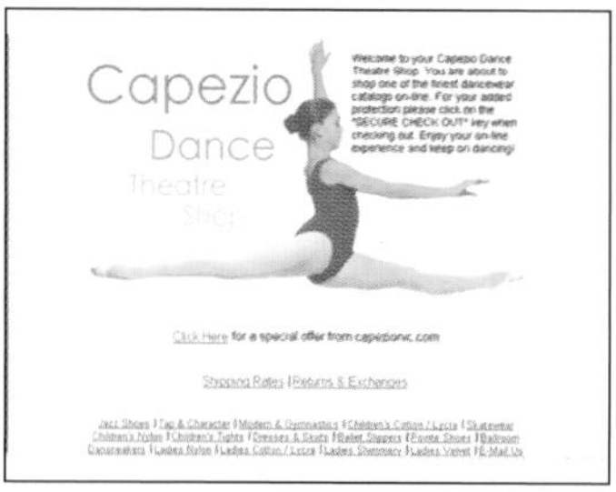

Whether you're a prima ballerina or flamenco is your forte, Capezio Dance Theatre Workshop has the dance and exercise gear to keep you on your toes. Get the leotards, unitards, jazz sneakers, and point shoes you need for rehearsals and performances. When your items arrive, test them gently—Capezio's strict return policy says no refunds on anything that looks broken in.

Overtons.com www.overtons.com

Yes, it's got the bathing suits and water wings you'll find at every other sporting goods site, but where else are you going to find doggie life preservers, boat engine parts, and barefoot waterskiing gear? Overtons.com can even deliver a boat to your home. Ahoy, me hearties!

Big Fitness.com www.bigfitness.com

Exercise your clicking finger by picking out stationary bikes, dumbbell racks, pulse monitors, and fat analyzers at Big Fitness.com. You may get a workout sifting through the site's low-tech interface, but not enough to break a sweat. Click through to the Reebok Store for sleek elliptical trainers and treadmills—and throw away that candy bar!

Speedo www.speedo.com
Don't worry: not all of Speedo's swimsuits are of the grape-smuggling variety. In fact, most of the gear seems to be designed for folks who don't confine their water activity to lounging around the pool. In addition to racing suits, there's also stuff like snorkel sets, swim stroke monitors, bathing caps, and radio watches. The prices are a little steep, but keep in mind that these products are made to last.

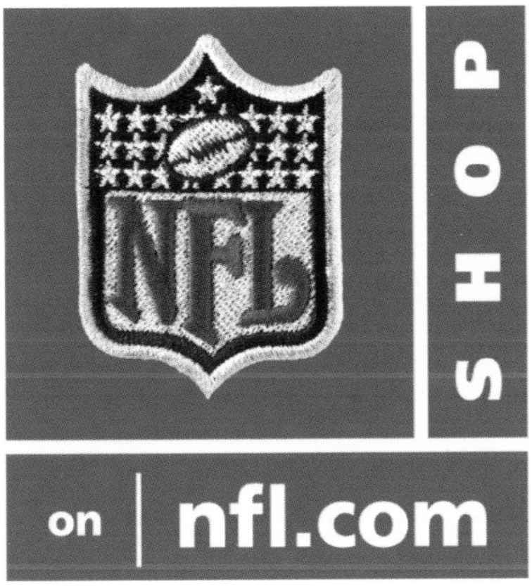

NFL Shop
www.nflshop.com
Armchair quarterbacks rejoice! Be a part of the gridiron action with official NFL Shop essentials, like the inflatable Chicago Bears chair or the personalized Dallas Cowboys jersey. There are even tie-dyed team T-shirts for the hippie sports fan up the street (not that you'd ever hang out with him, but still).

Workout Warehouse www.workoutwarehouse.com
You don't need to spend a lot of money to get in shape, as evidenced by the Workout Warehouse Web site. It's got home fitness equipment at deep discounts right from the manufacturer. Whether you're in the market for a NordicTrack skier, a Pro-Form treadmill, or an Image stationary bike, you're bound to find a bargain. Check out the installment payment plans if you're buying a big-ticket item.

LiveToPlay www.livetoplay.com
If you need outdoor gear but don't want to pay outrageous prices, LiveToPlay is a good starting point. This jam-packed auction site lets you bid on everything from skateboards to ski boots and camping stoves direct from such well-known retailers as Jansport, Motorola, and Airwalk. Bidding for such desirable merchandise can be a sport unto itself; be prepared to meet some formidable competition!

BUYGOLF.COM www.buygolf.com
Don't fool yourself, kid; golf isn't just a game, it's an industry. A peek at this Web site makes it clear within the first few clicks. Hawking everything from day schools for beginners to personal driving ranges for zealots, BUYGOLF.COM has items for every member of the family, including experts and lefties. If you've got a set of clubs to spare, auction them off at the linked Golf Club Exchange page.

Tickets

Tickets.com www.tickets.com
Whether you're willing to fly halfway around the world to see Barbara Streisand or are just too lazy to drag your butt over to the local ticket kiosk, this Web site can help. It has tickets to sporting events, cruises, concerts, and museums. If you don't see what you want, head for the auction page, where you can do battle for the last two Ricky Martin seats in the entire Midwest.

Ticketmaster www.ticketmaster.com
Ticketmaster remains the biggest ticketing agency in the U.S. That's both good and bad; on the upside, you can get tickets to nearly any large event in the nation in music, sports, and the arts. On the downside, you'll have to pay Ticketmaster's considerable service charge every time. Still, for selection and reliability, the site can't be outdone.

moviefone.com www.moviefone.com ⓒ
Wait in line for hours to get tickets to the new Scorcese picture? Fuhgettaboutit. You're better off visiting moviefone.com, where you can purchase tickets in advance and catch up on movie news and reviews. Purchasing tickets this way will cost you a little extra, but the lure of guaranteed seats just might be worth it.

CultureFinder.com www.culturefinder.com ⓒ
Tickets for Cher? Don't be gauche. Dial up CultureFinder.com for the really hot ticket in town: flamenco dancer Andrea del Conte. Log on here to find out about ballet, theater, and opera performances in your area. CultureFinder.com has special ticket offers on events all over the country, plus loads of articles on the art forms. There are even crash courses in every discipline for the culturally curious. Finally, a coherent plot summary of *I Pagliacci!*

Soldout.com www.soldout.com ⓓ

SOLD·OUT.COM™

When Spice Girls tickets sell out in 12 minutes, it's time to develop a new strategy for getting into the events you lust after. Unlike Ticketmaster, which sells tickets on a first-come, first-served basis, Soldout.com searches out tickets from unique sources, including season ticket-holders who may not want their seats. Is it scalping? Not quite. Skip the online auctions section here; we found very few tickets up for bid.

Aloud.com www.aloud.com ⓒ
Whether you're a tourist or a local, Aloud.com is a must-visit for concertgoers in the United Kingdom. This British version of Ticketmaster actually has a lot more to offer than The Lord of the Service Charge; you'll find a venue guide, an e-mail alert service, and a hot events calendar here, as well as incredibly well-written customer reviews.

Toys

Totally Fun Toys www.totallyfuntoys.com
Guaranteed to turn your kid into a Rhodes scholar (well, not really), Totally Fun Toys lets you take your pick of educational toys like K'NEX building sets, Furga ethnic dolls, and sponge painting kits. Parents who are shopping for gifts will appreciate the toy recommendations and the advanced search options page, which narrows down the wide selection of toys into a neatly tailored list. If Junior hates the Darda Turbo Scorcher you bought him (or already has it), be sure to call the site's toll-free number within 15 days to let them know you're sending it back. Otherwise, you'll have to pay a 15% restocking fee.

Just Pretend www.justpretend.com
Remember playing dress up when you were a kid? Now you can buy play clothes for your kids online! Just Pretend offers tools that encourage make-believe, like a spy kit, complete with disguises, secret messages, and survival gear, and capes and masks for budding superheroes. There are also costumes (for would-be clowns, police officers, and fairies) for kids aged 5-12 and a limited line of toys that foster "open-ended play."

DisneyStore.com www.disneystore.com
Unions want to bomb it, France wants to deport it, but as long as children continue to populate the Earth, Disney is here to stay. And after all, who are you to deny your kid a Tarzan & Jane Swingin' Gift Set or Tigger Musical Bouncing Santa? Brace yourself for a letdown, though: the content here is awfully limited. You can, however, send a Pooh-Gram (a bear, candy, and card customized for any occasion) or book your vacation to Disneyland or Disneyworld here.

BITSANDPIECES.COM www.bitsandpieces.com
BITSANDPIECES.COM's mission is to confound. The enigmatic site hawks puzzles of all kinds, from the 13,200-piece jigsaw to those frustrating wooden Japanese boxes that are so hard to open. There's also a Puzzle Mart section, which offers special items at a 25 to 50% discount, and the Puzzle Arcade, which lets you try your hand at solving a variety of online conundrums.

Mattel.com www.shopmattel.com ⓢ

From the company that brought us Chatty Cathy, Matchbox, and Barbie comes a new generation of toys and games, all souped up and cyber-ready. Shop here for the HotWheels Tattoo Designer CD-ROM, the IntelPlay Computer Microscope, or the Barbie Gotta Groove game. All of the toys come with an amazing one-year return policy (excluding software and games).

toysmart.com www.toysmart.com ⓒ ⓓ

A site that's dedicated to finding just the right toy for each and every child. Instead of offering a jumbled collection of educational toys for bewildered parents to sort through, this store divides its merchandise into sensible categories like age, brand, interest, and product. There are even aisles devoted to home school educators and public school teachers, as well as a toy guide for children with disabilities.

Red Rocket www.redrocket.com ⓒ ⓓ

Powered by Nickelodeon and featuring a ton of merchandise inspired by Nick characters, Red Rocket carries loads of toys, searchable by brand name. That's right: no more sifting through stupid old board games when your kid wants Pokémon; this site takes you right to the source. Reviews about the toys from real kids make the site fun to surf.

barbie.com www.barbie.com

The famed femme with the infamous proportions has a spot in cyberspace where you can preview upcoming Barbie collections, shop for Barbie software, and check out the latest additions to the Barbie empire. (Did you know she has a jet?) Of course, a huge variety of dolls are available for purchase, from the vintage Spring in Tokyo Barbie (around $50) to the Jewel Essence Barbie, with designer duds courtesy of Bob Mackie (at a cool $400).

NextPlanetOver www.npo.com

If the mention of manga, Boba Fett, or the Sandman gets you into heated arguments over arcane trivia, read on. NextPlanetOver is the site for "comics and cool stuff," including, but not limited to, sci-fi and fantasy. You'll find current and old editions of comics, graphic novels, toys, books, and T-shirts here. Ongoing chats with featured artists, such as Neil Gaiman (creator of *Sandman*), let you ask nagging questions, or you can debate with others on the message boards.

Family Wonder www.familywonder.com

Yes, you can control what your kids watch on TV! Go to Family Wonder to find fun videos tailored to your child's age group. The site also offers music and toys, deals for under $10, and articles with advice on how to turn video time into quality time. Satisfaction is guaranteed, and returns can be made for up to 30 days.

KidstuffRecords.com www.kidstuffrecords.com

"Bananas in Pajamas" only satisfies for so long. When you (or your child) need a change, KidsstuffRecords.com has 80,000 other sing-alongs, lullabies, and soundtracks for him or her to listen to. The site also has audio books for children, pre-teens, and even adults—the perfect solution to car trip boredom. So bag the Bananas and get some *Blue's Clues*, Bach, or Bradbury.

KBkids.com www.kbkids.com

Whether your children favor cuddly stuffed animals or terrifying monster models, they'll be more than satisfied with KBkids.com. In addition to an exhaustive amount of merchandise, this toy store has parenting clubs, contest giveaways and message boards, plus free shipping for orders over $30. A little boring as toy sites go, but the prices and selection just can't be beat.

Imaginarium www.imaginarium.com
Featuring an audio guide that sounds a lot like Cookie Puss, Imaginarium will guide you through its fabulous shelves of educational toys with a minimum of prodding. Each product that's sold here is accompanied by a handy logo explaining its benefit, making it easy to find toys designed to develop a child's visual, social, or motor skills. Jam-packed with neat-looking stuff like dinosaur puzzle kits, nursery trampolines, and solar-powered cash registers.

AnotherUniverse.com www.anotheruniverse.com
We've all got our obsessions, and if yours include sci-fi, *Star Trek*, or Xena, it's time to travel to AnotherUniverse.com. You'll find tons of collectibles and comics, from Danger Girl action figures to *Star Trek* phasers. When you've finished shopping, dive into reams of articles treating such pressing subjects as the pulled graduation episode of *Buffy the Vampire Slayer* and the scientific merit of *The X-Files*. Need we say more?

ZanyBrainy.com www.zanybrainy.com ⓒ
Want to know what your kids want for Christmas? Ask a "kidsultant" for gift-buying advice at ZanyBrainy.com. The site has some great features, like the Try Me! section, which allows you to actually play with several interactive toys simply by clicking your mouse.

FAO Schwarz www.faoschwarz.com
A giant singing clock, an army of frantic, animated animals, and swarms of screaming children: anyone who has witnessed the chaos of an FAO store will thank his lucky *Star Wars* for this Web site. Choose toys from more than 25 categories or search the recommendation feature (broken down by age) to find a great gift. Should that Buzz Lightyear figure snap in the hands of your precious little monster, return it to one of their 42 stores or mail it back for a refund.

Bear St. www.bearst.com ⓢ
You'll actually find a lot more than bears at Bear St., which is brought to you by teddy-bear specialists Gund; there are also furry jungle cats, monkeys, and dogs, among other things. Need a stuffed animal pronto? Relax, they can ship overnight internationally.

SmarterKids.com www.smarterkids.com ⓒ

SmarterKids.com™

Kids grow out of books faster than shoes—get the right fit from preschool to high school at SmarterKids.com. Parents and teachers offer their insights on the best tools for tots, with an emphasis on books and printed learning matter. Special features for supplemental instruction can be found in the 'zine-like Parents Center, which is full of advice, articles, and activities.

eHobbies www.ehobbies.com
Stocked with miniature cars, trains, airplanes, boats, and rockets, eHobbies is a community and a store for the serious hobbyist. Shop for anything under the sun (model trains, rocketry, tools), chat with other hobbyists, join a club, or read articles about everything you need to get started in a particular hobby field.

areyougame.com www.areyougame.com
If your mission in life is to erase that nasty rumor about what Miss Scarlet did in the conservatory with the candlestick, this Web site is for you. It's got all your favorite games and puzzles from childhood (remember Uno, Cootie, and Blockhead?), as well as the newfangled playthings your kids are always pestering you for (bet you'll be stealing their Electronic Grand Slam Baseball within a week or two).

eToys www.etoys.com (C)
EToys is designed for parents in panic; this is the place to go when you absolutely must find your child the latest, greatest action figure, computer game, or monster truck. For anyone who's clueless on what exactly a Teletubby or a Pokémon is, there's also an information section at the bottom of the page, with definitions of the most popular toys of the moment.

Birthday Express.com www.birthdayexpress.com
Billing itself as "the ultimate party source," this Web site can help you plan every last detail of your kid's birthday party, right down to the Scooby-Doo napkins. BirthdayExpress.com specializes in theme parties, hawking party favors, invitations, balloons, candles, and tablecloths emblazoned with every toy and cartoon character under the sun, including Madeline, the Teletubbies, and Barbie, plus 100 others.

NoodleKidoodle.com www.noodlekidoodle.com (C) (S)
Oodles and oodles of poodles and noodles. Selling only non-violent and gender-neutral games and toys for kids from ages 0 to 12+, NoodleKidoodle.com lets you browse by age, category, brand, or character (Scooby-Doo, Barney, Elmo, etc.) for toys both parents and kids can live with. The fabulous selection here includes CDs, puzzles, and nature toys as well.

Index

Credits

Editor-in-Chief Rula Razek

Assistant Editor Krista Prestek

Sales Associate Jeni Henaghan

Designer Francesca Richer

Picture Editor Megan McEntire

Writer-Researchers Stephanie Dempsey, Patrick Enright, Rachel Neumann, Alexis Wichowski

Copy Editor Patrick Enright

Intern Rana Razek

internet cool guide: Shopping

16 West 22nd Street, New York, NY 10010
www.internetcoolguide.com
www.teneues.com

The Web sites and reviews in internet cool guide: Shopping were selected and written by an independent and unbiased editorial team. None of the sites included have paid to be listed. Some, however, have chosen to include a logo next to their review, for which we have charged a handling fee.

Certain Web site information, selections, or material contained in internet cool guide: Shopping may no longer be current at the time of publication because the sites in question are updated and revised on a regular and continuing basis.

While we strive for utmost precision in every detail, we cannot be held responsible for any inaccuracies, neither for any subsequent loss or damage arising.

ISBN 3-8238-5445-3

First Edition

Printed in Germany